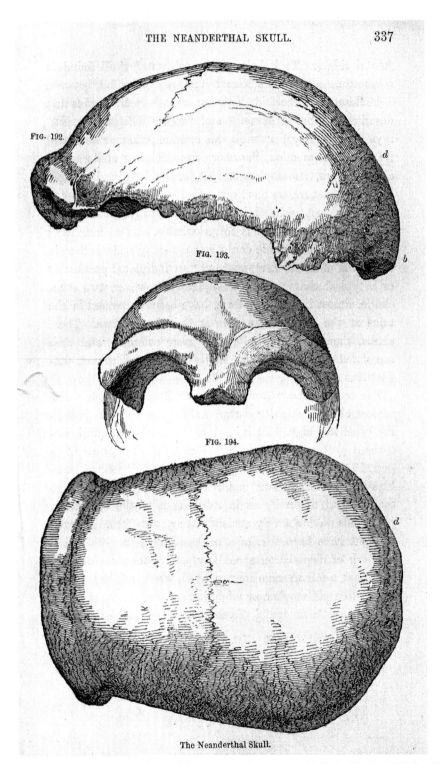

The Neanderthal Skull.

The Neanderthal skull, the only fossil hominid skull known in 1865 (Lubbock, 1869, fig. 192)

DARWIN'S PUPIL:

The place of Sir John Lubbock, Lord Avebury (1834–1913)
in late Victorian and Edwardian England

Michael Thompson

Published by

**MELROSE
BOOKS**

An Imprint of Melrose Press Limited
St Thomas Place, Ely
Cambridgeshire
CB7 4GG, UK
www.melrosebooks.com

FIRST EDITION

Copyright © Michael Thompson 2009

The Author asserts his moral right to
be identified as the author of this work

Cover designed by Matt Stephens

ISBN 978 1 906561 44 4

Printed and bound in Great Britain by:
CPI Antony Rowe. Chippenham. Wiltshire

Books by this Author

Dedication

To Ann Elizabeth, my wife for 44 years

Contents

List of figures in *Darwin's Pupil*

PREFACE

As a boy who spent the school holidays with my grandparents (my grandfather, born in 1867, was a patriarchal man married to a devout and pious lady who bore the brunt of the housework and wrote copious letters, often to dictation), I learnt to have an empathy and understanding of Victorian life. They had had seven children from 1895, but the background of an industrious, devoted wife with a somewhat hypochondriacal husband evoked the Victorian ethos to a remarkable degree, albeit at a lower social level than that of Lubbock. This was one factor that attracted me to write the present brief account of aspects of his life's work at a rather earlier date than that of my grandparents.

I had the privilege of attending the late Glyn Daniel's lectures in 1950 on historical archaeology; the subject was brought to life again when I discovered the travel notebooks of General Pitt-Rivers in the old Ministry of Works which led in due course to a short biography of the General. He owed his appointment as Inspector to an Act derived from Lubbock's Bill on Ancient Monuments. Lubbock himself became the son-in-law of the General after his marriage to his daughter Alice. More recently Lubbock has become a figure of special interest because of the Darwin connection – the central theme of the present book.

The material for Lubbock is abundant: he published profusely and his diaries and many letters to him have been deposited in the British Library. Moreover a large two-volume biography was published by Horace Hutchinson, who knew him personally, the year after his death. There is further information about his work by several authors in a work edited by his daughter, Ursula Grant Duff, in two editions of 1924 and 1934, the centenary edition. Apart from the manuscript material in the British Library, Emma Darwin's diary in the Cambridge University Library has many references to his visits, as we would expect. The link to Darwin is of course the crucial element in his life, and so in this book.

With this large volume of material available it did not seem that a full-scale biography was necessary or desirable. However, there should be some assessment of his place in Victorian and Edwardian England, especially as his reputation has not fared as well as it deserves. The wide range of his activities makes it difficult for one person to cover them, especially a non-scientist like the author. I hope that the essential features have been presented in a new way and that we can see this remarkable man in the round without concealing any of the warts or exaggerating his gifts.

Note. Mark Patton's *Science, Politics and Business in the Work of Sir John Lubbock* (Ashgate, 2007) regrettably only came to my notice when we had gone to press, and so it has not been used as it so patently deserves.

M. W. Thompson
Cambridge, 2008

ACKNOWLEDGEMENT:

The British Library and Cambridge University Library, for the use of manuscripts in both collections: the Lubbock papers and diaries in the former and the diary of Emma Darwin in the latter.

1. The Background

The earliest six-inch Ordnance Survey maps (sheets 16 SW and 28 NW) of Kent (an area now in Greater London) show the villages of Farnborough and Downe when the houses of High Elms and Downe were still occupied by, respectively, Sir John Lubbock and Charles Darwin. The distance between the two is ten inches on the map; that is just over a mile and a half on the ground, High Elms lying to the north east of Downe House, and so presumably a young athletic man could walk or ride from one to the other in 35 minutes or so. The parish boundary of Farnborough skirts the north side of High Elms which therefore, strictly speaking, is within Downe parish, so Darwin's references to Lubbock as 'My Neighbour' are understandable if a little stretched. The diary of Emma Darwin, his wife, in the 1850s refers to visits by 'the Lyells', 'the Huxleys', 'the Hookers' staying for two or three days, but less to Lubbock snr and son who presumably could come over in a morning or afternoon. There is every reason to suppose that that is just what he did when he was studying natural history with Darwin at that time. A track is shown from outside High Elms straight to Downe village.

The Lubbocks always had a house in London; it was there that Lubbock jnr was born in 1834. High Elms, a large three-storeyed structure with Regency rather than Gothic leanings, now burnt down, was constructed or reconstructed in 1840 according to Pevsner[1], so Lubbock jnr must have been a child of five or six before it was sufficiently completed to allow occupation.

John Lubbock snr perhaps foresaw a large family to accommodate when he set up this grand seat in an area which was still rural but only ten miles from the City in which lay his private bank, reachable by the growing rail network. In his son's time the commuter station was Orpington. Lubbock snr had eleven children, of whom he was the second, being the eldest son between two sisters, as one can see in the family tree published by Hutchinson[2]. This was no doubt part of a fairly general movement out of London to an area rather favoured by bankers, according to Cassis. The size of the house allowed an active social life where balls were held, as mentioned by Emma Darwin who evidently regarded it as a grander establishment than that at Downe House. Lubbock jnr seems to have held house parties there with guests up to the social level of Gladstone as we learn from Hutchinson.

John jnr's diary starts in 1852[3] when he was 18 and shows a healthy, normal young man playing cricket and fond of dancing, with a critical eye on his female partners. He was already a man of science, making visits to the British Museum. He was at High Elms until marriage in 1856 obliged him to move out, only returning at his father's death in 1865. He inherited the house and bank and this remained his permanent home until he acquired Kingsgate Castle in 1902[4]. We must return to his early life and try to assess some of the crucial factors that determined his later life.

fig 1. Portrait drawing of Lubbock aged 33 (Hutchinson, 1914, frontispiece)

The starting point must be Sir John William Lubbock (1808–1865), third baronet, father of the subject being discussed. Eton and Trinity College, Cambridge, partner in his father's bank, Fellow of the Royal Society, 1829, later its Treasurer and Vice President: the *Dictionary of National Biography* tells us a great deal. For both his father and his elder son, the private bank in the City was always the source of the prosperity of the family wealth. Lubbock snr was a scientist, but a 'hard' scientist because his subjects were mathematics and astronomy. His son became 'soft' – that is, his inclination was towards the life sciences, biology and botany; not that the father disapproved of or obstructed his son's interests. Unlike his father, Lubbock jnr did not complete his studies at Eton, nor did he attend a university, although he compensated for this in later life as MP for the new University of London, serving in its Senate as well as acting as its Vice Chancellor.

High Elms

fig 2. High Elms across the lake (Hutchinson, 1914, p. 192)

The whole ethos of a family whose father was a distinguished scientist and something of a martinet must have affected all its members. A scientific attitude was in the air, and must have been encouraging to both families – so near each other – to a social life in common, as the diary suggests. Darwin lived a fairly secluded life, only occasionally going to London or to spas for health treatment. Both families had young children, which was likely to give them common interests. Darwin came to Downe in September 1842 – that is, probably a year or two after the Lubbocks went to High Elms. The early association of the two is illustrated by the story of the microscope bought by Darwin in 1848 for Lubbock snr to give to his son, Lubbock jnr, authenticated by reference to the receipt in Darwin's *Correspondence*[5].

More important from career point of view was that at Downe House the young man met Charles Lyell, Thomas Huxley and Sir John Hooker, powerful men in the academic field who could ease his passage to the Royal Society (elected in 1858) and Athenaeum. This is not to belittle his abilities, nor to suggest that his achievements did not fully deserve worldly success; his scientific papers started flowing from 1853, mainly on insects, his lifelong interest.

As we might expect, we have very little information on the sort of help and guidance that Darwin gave him before the volumes of *Correspondence* of Darwin published by Cambridge University Press started coming out (still in progress) from which snippets of telling information may be gleaned. Here are examples:

> In a letter of July 1851:
> 'the eldest son of Sir John Lubbock, my neighbour who has a passion for dissecting insects' (vol. 5, 103).

> In a letter of November 1852:
> 'I have a neighbour who is very anxious to see the work; he is the son (very young) of Sir J. Lubbock, the great astronomer and Banker, who has taken up the smaller Crustacea with great zeal and will soon publish ...' (vol. 5, 103).

In a letter of 7th April 1859 (that is before the *Origin of Species* was published that autumn) to Wallace discussing Natural Selection:

> 'My neighbour and excellent naturalist J. Lubbock is enthusiastic convert' (vol. 7, 279).

When Lubbock was proposing to move to Brighton where his wife's parents lived, Darwin wrote:

> 'how much I enjoyed your friendship and what a loss your absence would be to me ...' (vol. 9, 235).

In June 1865 in a letter to Lubbock: 'The latter half of your book has been read out aloud to me and the style is so clear and easy (we both think it perfection) that I am now going back to the beginning.' The book referred to is *Prehistoric Times* and he goes on to say: 'Though you have necessarily only compiled the materials the general result is most original. But I ought to keep the term original for your last chapter which has struck me as an admirable and profound discussion. It has quite delighted me for now the public will know what kind of man you are which I am proud to think I discerned a dozen years ago.' Lubbock was about to stand for Maidstone (without success) and Darwin, who disapproved, commented in his last paragraph:

'I do sincerely wish you all the success in your election and in politics but after reading the last chapter Oh Dear Oh Dear Oh Dear.' The letter ends, 'Yours affectionately Ch. Darwin' (vol. 13, 182). This very revealing letter shows the close relationship between the two men and the long period of time it had lasted.

The letters are important for they show that Lubbock was primarily a biologist, not an archaeologist or anthropologist, and this was always so. This should be remembered in the discussion of his first two books in the following chapters. His *chefs-d'oeuvres* in this field came afterwards. The two books in their later editions were like a Greek chorus in the background.

Banking was Lubbock's life blood, in that it provided the means to maintain a high standard of life, extensive travelling and his scientific activities. He was a wealthy man by the standards of the time, leaving £375,000 (perhaps equivalent to £15 million in modern terms although no real conversion is possible). The whole issue of Victorian and Edwardian banking has been treated sociologically by Youseff Cassis, 1984, written originally in French but available in translation. The Lubbocks play a prominent part in the story as indeed we might expect.

The British banking system changed almost unrecognisably after the war of 1914–18: today a handful of large joint-stock banks dominate the scene, but before 1914 the predominant form of bank was the private deposit bank. The richest banks were merchant banks in a category above the private banks to which the Lubbocks belonged: Lubbock and Foster, later Curtis and Robarts. They went through various changes in the partnerships, and following Lord Avebury's death in 1913 his bank was taken over in 1914 by the well-known bank that still exists, Coutts. According to Cassis, in 1860 Lubbock's bank had capital of £500,000 and deposits of £2,913,000.

Some of the most interesting parts of Cassis' book are the sociological study of the bankers of the period. The Lubbocks fitted very well into the pattern, living in the favoured area of west Kent, ten miles from the City. Lubbock snr, educated at Eton and Trinity College, Cambridge, demonstrated the general tendency of the education of bankers' sons. Lubbock jnr, being at Eton, was a norm but missing out on university was less common and we shall see had important consequences.

One of the features of the profession was the large amount of spare time that it allowed. To quote Cassis, 'It is a profession which, whilst yielding substantial income, leaves to those that exercise it an appreciable amount of free time.' The large amount of time Lubbock spent travelling, writing, chairing numerous societies and attending and speaking at Royal Commissions, London University, quite apart from the House of Commons or Lords, is understandable against this background, and from 1882 he took no active part in running the bank.

Lubbock occupied a prominent position in City banking, being President of the Institute of Bankers. The particular reform associated with Lubbock's name is the creation of a Country Clearing Bank through which cheques could be cleared, hitherto only possible for

City banks who had in fact been doing it for some time. Other banks had previously to send cheques to the relevant bank individually.

Banking is bound to some extent to affect the personality, as one can see even today. With a private bank this is even more so because the risks are greater. The private banker takes large sums of money from his clients so a loss of confidence by the clients can lead to a run on it of a type we have recently seen, which was more common in the nineteenth century. Scandal and views which are sharply discordant with those of the Establishment can lead to a loss of confidence and a clamour for return of deposits, as much as an ill-judged investment. It tends to affect one's outlook on life; an academic like Thomas Huxley was free to say what he liked whereas a banker like Lubbock had to watch his words, and what he does say can often be rather trite. One has the feeling with Lubbock's writing, so often addressed to the general reader as much as the scientific public, that he is reassuring them that he is sound and trustworthy. He rarely expresses strong feelings and when he does, as with Irish Home Rule, it is probably the view of the majority. It was Gladstone, not he, that was out of step. We see it more clearly in his essays in later life, but it is present in his earlier work. He preferred to transmit rather than put forward new ideas. There are certain exceptions and I am not in any way seeking to denigrate him.

Education, or the lack of it, was a prime consideration throughout the life of Lubbock, Sir John Lubbock bart. from the death of his father in 1865 and Lord Avebury from 1900. His biographer tells us that he was eight years old when he was sent to a private school at Abingdon, where his fellow pupils were apparently decidedly aristocratic, but whether this made him feel plebeian we do not know. He had the gift of being able to associate with all the numerous gradations of English society in later life, so the experience may have been useful.

After three years at his prep school he was sent to Eton where he stayed for three years, no doubt sufficient time for Eton to leave its characteristic impress upon him. At that time Eton's curriculum consisted of Latin and Greek, with one lesson in geography confined mostly to Italy, Greece and Asia Minor. Arithmetic, modern languages, science and drawing were not regarded as essential parts of education, so

Lubbock was perhaps not so broken-hearted to leave the school early at the age of 14 in 1848. The reason for this according to Hutchinson was that his father, deprived of the assistance of his partners due to illness, required help in the City office of the bank.[7]

He then entered into a period when he was commuting to the City while still only a boy. It was an unhappy time, so he tells us, although perhaps the most formative part of his education, which was self-education; he may have been teased by his more fully educated colleagues. This was the time when he associated with, one might say was taught by, Darwin, which was only a part of a vigorous regime of self-education. He himself gave his curriculum, recorded by Hutchinson (p. 30), on Christmas Day 1852, when he was aged eighteen.

Rising at 06.30 he read psalms and studied mathematics with his father before breakfast. 8.30 to 9.00 Natural History; 9–9.30 Prayers; 9.30 to 11.30 work with microscope; 11.30 to 13.00 read natural history; 1.00 to 1.30 lunch; two hours outside, then half an hour of poetry and half an hour of political economy; 16.30–17.00 tea; up to 17.30 more science, half an hour of natural history. 18.00 to 19.15 history; 19.15 to 20.00 whist; 20.00 to 20.30 history; 20.30 to 21.30 mathematics; 21.30 to 22.00 sermons ('if I read them any later they invariably send me to sleep and as it is I cannot always keep awake'); 22.00 to 23.30 German ('which is the only thing that keeps me awake'); 23.30 Prayers; 24.00 Bed.

The course obviously concentrates on natural science and the rest is subsidiary. No geography or French, nor Classics. The German is an indication of its importance then, dominating science – and indeed most subjects – and essential for natural history. Possibly like the late Harold Macmillan he had had a French nanny for he was fluent in it. Apart from teaching of mathematics by his father and no doubt some natural history by Darwin, it was completely self-educational. He certainly appears religious at this date whatever may have been his views later. He could presumably only follow this schedule on the days he did not go into the City to the Bank. Perhaps it was an ideal, for the cricket and dancing recorded in his diary could hardly be fitted into this timetable. As he was already publishing articles in the New Year he had evidently studied hard.

In 1862 Herbert Spencer, who had had a short stay with Lubbock, described in his *Autobiography* (vol. 2, p. 72) a day with him: various activities before breakfast, rapid glance at *Times* on way to station, reading some pages from a book he carried, banking in the morning, political business or scientific society after dinner. Spencer was astonished at his 'versatility' and his wife's 'vivacity'. The schedule of his self-education at the age of 18 he kept up in a different form throughout life.

The consequences of his self-education may be visible in some of his publications, particularly in the essays in the last years of life, with excessive quotation as if he was trying to emulate those who had what he did not have, to prove himself as it were. The question of the best 100 books that was first suggested at the Working Men's College, seems to demonstrate how well-read he was. This is not to sneer, for his self-education was highly successful and carried him through a rewarding life and he could not have done the science in any other way.

In considering the background factors that influenced his later life, clearly the innate or inherited ones cannot be ignored and may indeed be the most important ones – that is character and personality – albeit by far the most difficult to assess a hundred years after his death. We have to rely to a great extent on how he impressed those around him or those encountered by him in his work.

If we consider the large number of appointments he received, arranged to give the design of a keeled bowl in his later books (fig. 15), then it must be assumed he had qualities that were much in demand and were in fairly short supply since generally they were not solicited. He himself was surprised by invitations to stand for the Parliamentary seat of London University, and for its Senate or Vice Chancellorship, since he had no university degree. A good many of these requests are in the letters in the British Library. The fact is, Lubbock was one of Nature's chairmen or presidents, who could face controversy, even indeed London dock strikers, imperturbably or serenely (to use Hutchinson's adverb) and usually get his own way. It is a great gift which we may illustrate by a letter from his friend Grant Duff, quoted by Hutchinson:[8]

My dear Lubbock

You really must allow me to congratulate you on the way you managed those beasts of Ephesus [Corporation of Foreign Bondholders] yesterday It was a most finished piece of art-quite classical in its perfection I would not have missed it for a great deal ...

Hutchinson speaks of his 'serenity' and Darwin calls him 'amiable', and this combination of being agreeable at the same time as being imperturbable is a prominent aspect of Lubbock's personality. If we combine this with industrious, very sociable, intelligent, and with a remarkably retentive memory, we have a rough idea of the temperament of our subject.

Of the various factors that have been mentioned it would probably be wrong to say that this or another was the overriding one to determine his life; we are all the product of many different influences in our childhood and not the least is pure chance. The proximity of Darwin during his youth was purely accidental but evidently had major consequences.

Notes:

1. Newman, 271, in *West Kent* in Pevsner's *Buildings of England*. There is a photograph of High Elms in Hutchinson vol. 2, opposite p. 192.
2. Folder opposite page 1
3. British Library Reference to diaries: Add. 62679–84. There is a change in the style of diaries to volumes with lockable clasps, suggesting need for secrecy. At one point there is a scrawled diary in a normal notebook and one with a lockable clasp for the same dates.
4. Kingsgate Castle, Kent, in Hutchinson, photograph opposite p. 132, and see pp. 139–148. in vol. 2 and fig. 13 here.
5. *Correspondence*, vol. 4, p. 184.
6. Smart, 1979, p. 144.
7. Hutchinson, 1914, vol. 1, pp. 22–4.
8. Hutchinson vol. 1, 327.

2. The Origin of Species by Natural Selection

This chapter has been given the title of the famous book by Charles Darwin, not only because in 1859 the subject of our book, then aged 25, was still associated with his 'neighbour', Darwin, but because also it had a strong influence on him, much stronger than is often realised, but because it was an element leading to the publication of his first book in 1865, *Prehistoric Times*. We will try to see how this came about in this chapter and discuss the contents of the book in the next one.

The circumstances surrounding the publication of the *Origin* are well known and have been described many times, most recently by Janet Browne,[1] and it will not be necessary to repeat them here. Much of the thinking and observation that produced the book had been done years before; although Darwin had a text he had not published, no doubt because the climate of scientific opinion against continuous evolution had been unfavourable after its dismissal by Charles Lyell, the famous geologist and close friend of Darwin, in 1830 in the second volume of *Principles of Geology*.[2] Lyell had come down in favour of Georges Cuvier, the French anatomist, who thought there had been individual acts of creation for each species, ultimately a religious view.

What had precipitated publication was a letter from Alfred Russell Wallace (1823–1913) written in the Far East, setting out in a paper to prove a closely similar thesis to Darwin's theory of evolution by natural selection, causing (as might be expected) a considerable shock.[3] Darwin wisely consulted Lyell and Hooker and the upshot was that both Darwin and Wallace contributed a joint paper on this subject to the journal of the Linnaean Society in 1858.[4] Probably at this stage Lubbock first heard of natural selection for in the letter quoted above from Darwin to Wallace (p. 6) Lubbock was referred to as an 'enthusiastic convert' in April 1859. Meanwhile Darwin had been persuaded to publish the full text of *On the Origin of Species by means of Natural Selection*. A print run of 1,250 was issued in November and promptly sold out, so a second edition, hardly altered and more of a reprint, was issued in December, 1859. This edition is the one used here in the handy reprint published by Oxford University Press.

To someone looking at the fossil record of animals and plants or the whole structure of nomenclature with its kingdoms, families, orders, genera and species, they might suggest some kind of evolution or how else can one explain the evident relationships? A most convincing case for transmutation of species and so evolution had been made by Jean-Baptiste Lamarck (1744–1829) some years before the *Origin*. This had been magisterially examined in the second volume of *The Principles of Geology*, the part dealing with 'Organic' material, but rejected by Lyell.

The difficulty with any theory of evolution was how to explain the transition, the metamorphosis so to speak, with no intermediate or partially altered species. Genetics were quite unknown at that time. Darwin's success was due to how it came about, that carried conviction with most of his colleagues and indeed with most general readers.

It was change by 'variation', to use Lyell's expression. Every species produces varieties and sometimes the variety has an advantage that allows it to thrive and multiply, slightly altering until a point is reached where it can no longer interbreed with the parent species and so a new species is born. This never stops and is indeed the engine for creating the multiplicity of life. There is no way back and there is no spontaneous creation; all life is ultimately related to all other life. The natural selection of Darwin's title refers to the selection by nature of which varieties survive, and the parent species is removed from the scene by Malthusian principles. Nature is unbelievably prodigal with life and death as indeed is only too apparent in fertilisation and breeding: survival is hazardous, causing 'survival of the fittest' to use Spencer's phrase. We need not pursue these well-known matters except to say that it is not the process but the result itself, the evolution of all life, animal and vegetable, that is important for the biologist as indeed for the philosopher.

To understand the intellectual shock of the *Origin* we can do no better than read the original text; Darwin was not perhaps being deliberately dramatic but it certainly has that effect. The present writer on his first reading of the *Origin* found the world seemed a different place; his relationship to the living things around him had altered. If this book has this effect on the non-scientist it will be appreciated that for a naturalist or biologist who is closely studying living things and is daily confronted with evidence, like Huxley or Lubbock, the response must have been considerably stronger.

Two short passages from Darwin's chapter on the geological succession may be quoted to illustrate this:

> We can understand how it is that all the forms of life, ancient and modern, make together one general system; for all are connected by generation. We can understand from the continual tendency to divergence of character, why the more ancient a form is, the more it generally differs from those now living. Why ancient and extinct forms often tend to fill up gaps between existing forms, sometimes blending the two groups previously classed as distinct into one; but more commonly only bringing them a little closer together ... (pp. 308–9).

Or again:

On the other hand all the chief laws of palaeontology plainly proclaim, as it seems to me, that species have been produced by ordinary generation of forms having been supplanted by new and improved forms of life produced by the laws of variation still acting around us and preserved by Natural Selection ... (pp. 309–10).

It is heady stuff even for the general reader.

From the point of view of our subject of study the central question was, did evolution apply to man himself? It was implicit in the book that Darwin thought so, although he does not say so. The public and the press seized on this and, man's assumed progenitors being monkeys, it became an object of ridicule. At the meeting of the British Association for the Advancement of Science at Oxford in 1860, the year following the publication of the *Origin*, Huxley was provoked by the then Bishop of Oxford into a strong retort (several versions of the story exist). Darwin was not present, but Lubbock was on the platform and also spoke. The hooting of the Oxford undergraduates must have shocked him and perhaps led to his marked reticence on the subject subsequently.

We have now to assess the impact of Darwin's theory of evolution on Lubbock. The effect was profound on Huxley and others:

> ... the *Origin* in 1859 had the effect upon them of a flash of light to a man who had lost himself in a dark night, that suddenly reveals a road, which whether it takes him straight home at night certainly goes his way ...[5]

Huxley reviewed the *Origin* for the *Times* on Boxing Day 1859, already taking up a defensive stance.

Probably, almost certainly, the creation of the new journal, *Natural History Review*, or rather the adaptation of an existing Irish journal, owed its birth to the publication of the *Origin* a year before The first number of this quarterly journal appeared in January 1861.[6] The moving spirit was Huxley, although it had a multiple editorship which included both Lubbock and Busk. The first number had an article by Huxley entitled 'Relations of Man with the Lower Animals', a fair indication of how Huxley's thoughts were running and a preparation for *Man's Place in Nature.* The journal had a very short life and I know of only five annual volumes that appeared.

The significance of the journal for Lubbock was to record the expeditions that he made to study prehistoric remains on the Continent and in Scotland. There were five journeys between 1861 and 1864: October 1861, January 1862, July 1862, North American archaeology in January 1862 (not based on a visit) and 'Cave-men' in July 1854. It was a course in self-education on known prehistoric sites and he may not have had a book in mind yet.

It is suggested that they were prompted, like the new journal itself, by the *Origin*'s appearance in 1859. The sites were admirably described from a geological point of view by Lyell in his *Antiquity of Man with Remarks on the Origin of Species by Variation* in 1863, using in one case Lubbock's publication, so they were given the stamp of authority by the great geologist.[7] Evolution had opened, as it were, a great void of time yet to be filled with archaeological remains, with only these scanty remains known. It dawned on Lubbock that he was on the threshold of a new subject. Unfortunately Lubbock's diary is defective and not kept up because of the move from High Elms after his marriage in 1856, and in any case this was not the sort of subject he would have recorded in his diary. So our evidence is inferred from his actions, not from his own admission.

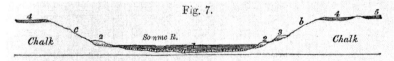

Fig. 7.

Section across the Valley of the Somme in Picardy.

1 Peat, twenty to thirty feet thick, resting on gravel, *a.*
2 Lower level gravel with elephants' bones and flint tools, covered with fluviatile loam, twenty to forty feet thick.
3 Higher level gravel with similar fossils, and with overlying loam, in all thirty feet thick.
4 Upland loam without shells (*Limon des plateaux*), five or six feet thick.
5 Eocene tertiary strata, resting on the chalk in patches.

fig 3. Lyell's section of Somme valley in Picardy, showing the two gravel terraces containing flint tools and bones of extinct animals (Lyell, 1863, fig. 7)

Darwinian evolution altered the perspective from the rather narrow one of the Scandinavian 'three-age' system based as it was on the classification of museum collections of essentially post-glacial material, for Scandinavia had been buried under the ice until c.10,000 years ago. The authentication by Prestwich of the hand-axes from the Somme gravels in early 1859[8] put the appearance of man back to when now-extinct animals lived. One can see this in Daniel Wilson's book on Scotland divided into four rigid parts on the Scandinavian system,[9] the fourth part being Christian, its very title – *Prehistoric Annals* – suggesting that Wilson was thinking in terms of the medieval annalist. Charles Lyell saw the consequences in 1863, and to his book we must now turn.

fig 4. Handaxe from Hoxne, Norfolk (Lubbock, 1869, figs, 197, 198)

An even closer link between Darwin and prehistory was Lyell's *On the Geological Evidences of the Antiquity of Man* (1863) since he had read the proofs of the *Origin* and it was indeed on the advice of Lyell and Hooker that Darwin had published it.[10] The 'geological evidences' of what we now call the 'Palaeolithic period' are central to its study. Lubbock created the name but Lyell created the context in which the remains were found and an outline chronology. He described the very limited physical fossil remains; there is no doubt that his book is a better one scientifically and intellectually than Lubbock's *Prehistoric Times*.

Another figure that must be mentioned, although perhaps more importantly later on, is Herbert Spencer. By origin an engineer and then editor of the *Economist*, he later supported himself by the proceeds of his prolific publications, particularly those on his System of Synthetic Philosophy covering biology, psychology, sociology. He was a bachelor living in London and had the distinction of being the only member of the X Club who was not a Fellow of the Royal Society. The X Club was a small dining club of scientists in the Royal Society who exercised considerable influence in it. Its members included Lubbock, Huxley and Busk. His relevance to our story was that he had the idea of a form of evolution from the 1840s and 1850s, some years before Darwin. His was however a more Lamarckian general form (from the simple to the complicated) than that of Darwin and so was not a rival but may have prepared the way to some degree for the *Origin*. It was more of a philosophical concept than based on observation.[11]

In the 1950s, when the late Glyn Daniel was writing, Darwin and evolution were under something of a cloud – at least in archaeological circles – from which he only emerged triumphantly later in the century, The wisdom of the time in later prehistory tended to play down Darwin and evolution as key figures. I did not always see eye to eye with them in this matter, so I hope this book will help to put them back more centrally.

Finally one may ask whether Lubbock was 're-enchanted' with the world described by George Levine in his book, with its unfortunate title *Darwin Loves You* which is nevertheless a serious work.[12] Huxley is the paradigm but Lubbock in his youth was closer than him to Darwin, to judge by the 'yours affectionately' letter ending, which in Victorian terms is a fairly intimate style. At Darwin's death Lubbock speaks of him in the diary as 'like a breath of sea air', which was regarded of health value in Victorian times. We know from Darwin's letter to Wallace in April 1859 that Lubbock was an 'enthusiastic convert' to natural selection and it is an easy passage from that to 'enchantment'. His sudden interest in prehistoric archaeology, with visits to the Continent and articles in the recently refounded *Natural History Review* leading to the book, are surely indications of a profound change of views that might be called 're-enchantment'. The last chapter of *Prehistoric Times*, which Darwin so greatly admired, is surely a harbinger of the scientific optimism that so characterises his later essays and lectures, which gave him such enthusiastic popularity in later life. This last chapter, together with one or two of the later essays, are reprinted as appendices at the end of this book.

Notes:
1. Browne, 2003
2. Lyell, 1830
3. Browne, pp. 13–14
4. *ibid.* pp. 34–5
5. L. Huxley, 1903, vol. 1, p. 245
6. *Natural History Review*, 1861–5, vol. 1, pp. 67–84
7. Lyell, 1863
8. Prestwich, 1859
9. Wilson, 1851
10. Browne, p. 76
11. *ibid*, pp. 184–5
12. G. Levine, 2006

3. *Prehistoric Times*

First published in 1865, drawing together the results of his travels to Scandinavia, Switzerland and France, just described, as had been suggested by the publishers, Williams and Norgate, it developed into something much more elaborate. It was Lubbock's first book, published when he was aged 31, and as there were seven editions between 1865 and 1913 it was clearly a commercial success. The second edition of 1869 was largely rewritten and had 70 extra illustrations and two extra chapters, an introductory one and another on the Pleistocene fauna associated with the Palaeolithic remains, inserted before describing them in chapter 9. I have used this edition throughout, from an inscribed copy presented by the author to the Society of Antiquaries. There were minor alterations in the later editions up to the seventh edition with coloured frontispiece, entirely out of date, and issued posthumously, for Lubbock did not even correct the proofs.

Lubbock made perfectly clear what had been his intention in the book apart from recording his travels:

The first appearance of man in Europe dates from a period so remote that neither history nor even tradition can throw any light on his origin or mode of life; some have supposed that the past is hidden from the present by a void, which time may probably thicken, but never can remove.

A new science, geology, has been born among us which deals with far more ancient things than any that have yet fallen within the province of archaeology.

Nor does there appear any reason why those methods of examination that have proved so successful in geology should not be used to throw light on the history of man in prehistoric times. Archaeology forms in fact the link between geology and history. (p. 2)

Charles Lyell had demonstrated in the *Antiquity of Man* (1863) from geological evidence which Lubbock took as read; it was the methods of geology that were to be used in the new science of archaeology. This is indeed the *leitmotiv* of the book: that we are dealing with an independent subject of study. He is describing stone, bronze and iron objects not to classify them as a collector (although he was a collector) but because they were the sources for studying prehistoric times. The book is weak on classification, one of the reasons why it has not survived so well as those of John Evans on stone and bronze tools,[1] but is full of ethnographic comparisons which seemed to offer a much deeper insight into life in 'prehistoric times', a matter to be discussed below ...

The foundation of the subject had been laid in Denmark when the 'three-age' system had been adopted by Thomsen to classify the material for display at the Copenhagen Museum. It was adopted first in Scandinavia and then in Europe generally. This was the system employed by Daniel Wilson[2] for Scotland in 1851 with a fourth addition of a Christian period. Lubbock also had four periods, created by subdividing the initial Stone Age into two, Palaeolithic and Neolithic, omitting the Christian period of course (pp. 2–3). It has proved a fundamental division ever since, although the modern reason for the division is based on the introduction of agriculture rather then whether the stone was ground and polished. It has been one of the preoccupations of prehistoric archaeologists since at least the time of Gordon Childe in the 1920s.[3]

Mention of Childe brings us to another point: both Lubbock's book and the *Dawn* were based, not on original excavation, but on travelling around in Europe, in Childe's case beyond, looking at museum and private collections, usually accompanied by experts from the particular region and visiting sites with excavators. What then was the difference: Childe had the advantage of the German concept of cultures and had a thesis which is in the title. Like the sun, civilisation arose in the east and its steady influences moved north and westward. Lubbock knew nothing of cultural areas and his main theses were that the subject of prehistoric archaeology existed and the three-age system applied all over. We might add also that a study of modern primitives ('savages') helped us understand the users of the ancient tools.

Even from the little we have referred to we may agree with Darwin and his wife (p. 6 above) it is clear, well-written and skillfully constructed; to whom was it directed? The commercial success of the book leaves little doubt that it was widely read and that there was a fairly large, well-educated readership that we know existed in Victorian England, and these no doubt Lubbock addressed for there was no serious professional class, but this subject would appeal to naturalists with varying interests. This is after all the class to which Lubbock himself belonged, who would understand and indeed expect Latin specific names and quotations, and authorities quoted in the original French.

With regard to the main text of the book, comment has often been made on the reversed chronological order of the chapters, clearly done quite deliberately. The flint tools from the river gravels found accidentally in the gravel pits are the most difficult contexts for the reader to easily understand. Moreover it is fairly standard practice in teaching to start from the known, the bronze daggers and swords, and move back to the less familiar. If you are looking back over your shoulder this is the order in which you see things. On Lyell's great principle of 'uniformitarianism', as nature worked in the present so it worked in the past, so again there was a lot to be said for starting, if not in the present, at least as near as possible.

In his travels, often with geologists like Prestwich or Busk, Lubbock had become used to vertical sections in the Somme valley or the peat of Scandinavia. The inverted order of the sequence reminds one of a geological section, with the grass and soil at the top and the levels of deposits following below. This is probably what Lubbock had in mind, but the text itself, with the inversion, reminds us of 'winding back the reel' by Marc Bloch. We have just been told that it is by the methods of geology that archaeology will be studied.

Before discussing the individual chapters, there is perhaps the most innovative feature of the book referred to in the title: *Prehistoric Times as Illustrated by Ancient Remains and the Manners and Customs of Modern Savages.* 'Savages' was the normal Victorian term for primitive peoples, and it may conflict less with modern taste to speak of primitives. It is as if he is already introducing the anthropology that we shall be discussing in the next chapter. The primitives are described in chapters 11, 12, 13 in the first edition, for they are an original feature, or chapters 13, 14, 15 in the second edition used here. The letter from Darwin quoted above, who read the last chapters first, suggests that it was the living 'modern savages' that interested him most. Biologists are used to living things rather than the mute hand-axes of the archaeologist. Both Darwin and Lubbock probably felt that way. There was an assumption by both that the way of life of the modern primitives resembled that of the vanished users of the ancient remains. Darwin after all had been deeply shocked by the Fuegans in South America, and Lubbock, who had no first hand experience of primitives, tended to adopt his attitude.

To illustrate this, the writer will venture to refer to his own experiences. In trying (successfully) to extract long strips from red deer antlers to show how it was done at the Mesolithic site at Star Carr, Yorkshire, it was clear that prolonged soaking made the drawn-out planing motion along the antler much easier.[4] The then professor pooh-poohed the idea that without vessels the Mesolithic hunters could have done this, but it was quite clear that modern primitives in Northern America and Siberia who worked in this kind of material took it for granted that soaking in water or urine was necessary. The matter was settled. Less certain results were achieved with the short Azilian harpoons split at the base, which it was suggested turned below the animal's skin, the attached shaft and line then being entangled in the surrounding vegetation, thus impeding the quarry's escape. There would be a sequence through the heavily barbed Magdalenian heads to the Azilian toggle heads in response to the ever-increasing vegetation. It makes a good story but the only parallel for this sort of toggle used not on marine animals but on land ones were iron toggles used by Negritos in south-east Asia. Let us finish with the familiar example of the hand-axe, often a handsome tool but with no clear traces of use. With no parallel tool among modern primitives (except possibly flake tools among the extinct Tasmanians) its use is likely to be a permanent enigma. We must bear in mind that the users were physically different from ourselves. This negative case shows how valuable such comparisons are.

To return to Lubbock's book, he was acutely aware of the value of making comparisons with tools and weapons of modern primitives or 'savages' as he called them. He does this in the archaeological part of the book and the three chapters on primitives, done precisely for this purpose. Had he concentrated on certain traits or on the 'manners and customs' of his title he would have moved into what was beginning to be called 'anthropology', as he did soon after this in 1870, and we shall be discussing that in the next chapter. In the cases of one or two of the peoples described he in fact did so.

Although he was disgusted by the primitives, as we would expect a banker to be, he did not regard them as having different origins, for it was good Darwinian belief that there was a common origin for all men. Some had just diverged in the race for survival.

We are already clear that the book is describing prehistoric archaeology in Europe and beyond; it is an ancestor of the works of Gordon Childe, Christopher Hawkes and Grahame Clark, the latter leading to *World Archaeology*. The British tradition in this subject has never been an insular one.

We may return to the main text; the first point is that if you are going backwards, where does prehistory begin? If the Classical period starts history in the Mediterranean, when did it start in northern Europe? In his first edition he plunged into uses of bronze and then the Bronze Age, but in the second edition used here we are told of an Iron Age at Nydam in Denmark and the great Halstatt cemetery in Austria. In his table we have Iron Age sites from Switzerland like La Tene. The table for the Halstatt cemetery, with its distinction between cremations and interments with associated grave goods, reveals the three-age system vividly. Lubbock had visited Halstatt between the two editions.

The chapters on the use of bronze and the Bronze Age follow and then the use of stone, followed by separate chapters on various features of the later stone age. The object is to justify or explain the system to people still very unfamiliar with it.

In the chapter on the use of bronze, the standard objects like daggers, spearheads and so on are described, as well as objects of gold and the woollen clothing from Danish barrows. The chapter on the Bronze Age uses Greek literary sources like Pytheas. Lubbock probably thought in Homeric terms, although he knew nothing of discoveries at Troy and Mycenae, but he visited Troy in 1872 in time for the third edition.[5] On questions of the knowledge of metals he wrote:

> ... it appears most probable that the knowledge of metal is one of those great discoveries which Europe owes to the East and that the use of copper was not introduced into our Continent until it had been observed that by the addition of a small quantity of tin it was rendered harder and more valuable. (p. 59)

This view would have been that generally held until recently and is clearly a line of thinking that, no doubt modified, is deeply rooted in the minds of European archaeologists.[6] In spite of lack of material and a firm chronology, and the culture concept, we are standing on familiar ground.

There follows the Stone Age which, with its ramifications, fills the next nine chapters; it cannot be too strongly emphasised that the backbone of the book is the Stone Age which perhaps because of its greater antiquity had a special attraction for Lubbock, even if he was uncertain about its periods in years. It is an area where he made the most fundamental contribution to the subject:

The Stone Age, however, falls naturally, as has been already said into two great divisions:

First. That of the Drift, which I have proposed to call the *Palaeolithic* or *Archaeolithic* period

Secondly. The later Stone Age for which I have suggested the term *Neolithic*, and in which the stone implements are more skillfully made, more varied in form and often polished.

Nowadays the division is fundamental, but the criterion for the change is the adoption of agriculture, not the stone-working. Lubbock was perhaps dimly aware of this factor since it was not only ground tools, but also the evident use of agriculture in the Swiss lake dwellings before the Danish kitchen middens, that is later when working backwards on his sequence.

We are then plunged into the stone tools of both periods. Although he was a collector he did not think in museum terms of classification, so in the figure opposite page 74 an odd medley of hand-axe, core, blade, polished axe and so on are displayed together. Ethnographic parallels are used freely as with Eskimo on page 93.

The next chapter is entitled 'Megalithic Monuments and Tumuli'; the big stones may be set in a circle or forming a chamber in a mound, the tumulus refers to the mound, with or without a chamber.

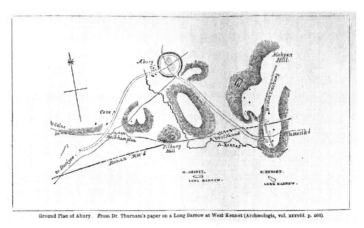

Ground Plan of Abury. From Dr. Thurnam's paper on a Long Barrow at West Kennet (Archæologia, vol. xxxviii. p. 405).

fig 5. Avebury plan to illustrate Roman road bending round Silbury Hill, showing the latter to be already there in Roman times (Lubbock, 1869, p. 124)

All over the Europe, we might indeed say all over the world, wherever they have not been destroyed by the plough or the hammer we find relics of prehistoric times: camps, fortifications, dykes, tumuli, menhirs, or standing stones, cromlechs or stone circles, dolmens or stone chambers etc, many of which astonish us by their magnitude. (p. 104)

There is no need to pursue all these structures. A plan opposite page 112 shows the Avebury circle and Silbury Hill to the south; it demonstrates that the Roman road from the west bends as it passes the great mound of Silbury, implying that the mound is older than the Roman road. Lubbock bought Silbury and parts of Avebury (in the latter case to prevent development), so he had a personal interest in the matter (fig. 5). It is an interesting case where Lubbock actually went into the field. Lubbock uses statistics in some cases, as when quoting Thurnam's records of skulls from long barrows and round ones in order to show that the skulls from long barrows are long compared with the round ones from round barrows (p. 129). Thomas Bateman's prolific excavations of barrows in Derbyshire furnished a wealth of information on the forms of burial, probably from the Bronze Age, although whether Lubbock knew this from the scanty grave goods but regarded barrows as Neolithic is not clear.

The sixth chapter deals with 'Ancient Lake Habitations of Switzerland' and in some ways is the climax of the book because of the excellent preservation of the waterlogged remains, not to mention the curious way of life led by the people living over the water by the lake shore. When the level fell in the winter the wooden piles apparently supporting residential structures above were revealed, although in some cases the piles may have acted as retaining posts for artificial islands like Irish crannogs:

> In consequence of the extraordinary dryness and cold of the weather during the winter months of 1853 the rivers of Switzerland did not receive their usual supplies and the water in the lakes fell much below the ordinary level so that in some places a broad strand was left uncovered. (p. 166)

fig 6. Keller's reconstruction of Swiss lake village; the piles were found but the superstructure is highly conjectural (Lyell, 1863, frontispiece)

They must have been known about before, but there was a sudden interest, so quite a literature was available ten years later when Lubbock visited and saw Dr Keller, the main investigator. Lubbock performed his usual but necessary service, bringing together known information on this as well as the Irish crannogs. In Switzerland, animal bones and plant remains survived so there was much information about agriculture (pp. 190–191). Many lakes produced evidence of occupation over a long period of time and Lubbock was able to produce evidence from all three ages in his tables. There was superposition of piles (p. 179). Most of the literature is in French and German but a full summary was published by Robert Munro in 1890.

> Denmark occupies a larger space in the history than on the map of Europe: the nation is greater than the country. … Many a larger nation might envy them the position they hold in science and in art and few have contributed more to the progress of human knowledge. (p. 215)

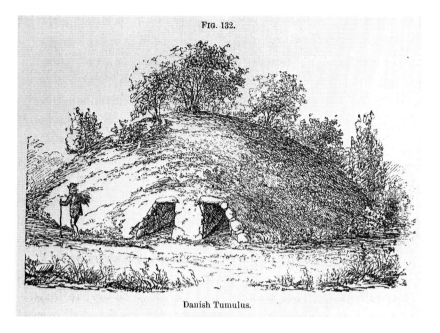

fig 7. Danish 'tumulus' with passage and chamber (Lubbock, 1869, fig. 132)

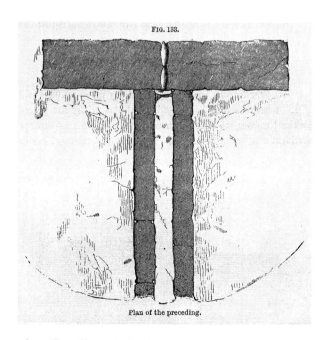

fig 8. Plan of 'tumulus' in figure 7 (Lubbock, 1869, fig. 133)

With this ringing tribute to the Danes and to the celebrated Museum of Northern Antiquities at Copenhagen, Lubbock starts his seventh chapter on the rather mundane subject of the Danish shell middens. However, first he describes the tumuli (some megalithic):

> The whole country appears to have been, at one time, thickly studded with tumuli. ... Fortunately the stones of which they are constructed are so large and so hard that their destruction is a laborious and expensive undertaking ... Many of the barrows indeed contain in themselves a small collection of antiquities and the whole country may be considered as a museum on a grand scale. The peat bogs, which occupy so large an area may almost be said to swarm with antiquities. All these advantages might have been thrown away but for the genius and perseverance of Professor Thomsen (pp. 215, 216).

FIG. 139.

Indian Dolmens.

fig 9. Modern 'dolmens' with 'portholes' in India (Lubbock, 1869, fig. 140)

We are introduced to the kitchen middens (*kjoekkenmodings*), which were at first taken for raised beaches but were identified by Professor Steenstrup as artificial deposits of kitchen waste containing bones and tools, hearths and marks of fire. The deposits are 3 to 5, occasionally up to 10, feet thick and sometimes 300 yards long. Essentially they are refuse heaps. A committee formed under Steenstrup had produced six reports, from which, with visits in 1861 and 1864, Lubbock drew his information.

Shell mounds found on the Moray Firth contained an early Christian pin and so must be later. Shell mounds are found in many parts of the world, the shells varying; in the Tagus mounds with which this writer was concerned the main shell fish were *Scrobicularia*, a sort of estuarine clam.[6]

The people of the Danish kitchen mounds had no knowledge of agriculture. The principal shells in mounds belong to oyster, cockle, mussel and periwinkle. Bones of wild but not domestic animals are found in them, as well as bird bones.

> It is perhaps not uncharitable to conclude that when their hunters were unusually successful the whole community gorged itself with food, as is the case with many savage races at the present time. (p. 233)

Lubbock goes on to compare them to the Fuegans of Tierra del Fuego which so shocked Darwin, as recorded in his Journal on the Beagle. Worsaae divides the Stone Age into three, with what we today call 'Mesolithic', a subdivision of the early Stone Age. Steenstrup disagreed and made them contemporary with the tumuli, while Lubbock disagreed and made them an early part of his Neolithic: most modern scholars would probably concur with Lubbock.

The chapter on North American archaeology, chapter 8, is in some ways an interruption in the smooth receding chronology of the work. Lubbock never went to America, but no doubt the extensive publication on the subject sponsored by the Smithsonian Institution of the Bureau of Ethnology in Washington could hardly be omitted from a general work on 'Prehistoric Times' which did not hesitate to use other overseas material.

According to Lubbock the civilisations of Central America were Bronze Age, while the east side of North America with which the Smithsonian dealt were in the Neolithic stage, and no doubt further north the Eskimos (Inuit) would have been Palaeolithic (the sort of equation that Sollas later made in too strong terms). The fact is, the three-age system was not helpful in North America and it was not until both Continents could be studied that a coherent account was reached.[7]

Nevertheless it was clear that significant changes of climate, with the associated changes in fauna, had also taken place in North America. In addition there was abundant evidence that an early population in the area had left evidence in the form of large earthworks with a range of functions. From the point of view of the next chapter Lubbock must have learnt of the work of Lewis Morgan on the Iroquois Indians, and two of his acquaintances, Christy, a fellow banker, and Tylor had had experience in Central America.

Chapter 9 deals with 'Quaternary Mammalia' – that is, the bones of the larger animals associated with the Palaeolithic remains, for it was the extinct animals, or those no longer living in the area, by which these tools and weapons had been dated from both the caves and river gravels. As they often revealed a very different climate from that of today they were major indicators of periods hotter or colder than today, especially of the Ice Age. The sites on the Somme or Dordogne were those mainly implicated. It may be remarked that as a biologist Lubbock was in his own field, and this chapter is one of the two new ones inserted in the second edition.

Identification of the animals to which the bones belonged threw light on two matters: what was hunted for food and the climate. Thus (p. 281) the mammoth or reindeer revealed a cold, even arctic climate, but hippopotamus or aurochs revealed a warmer, almost tropical climate. As the present-day fauna had existed since the end of the Ice Age (as in the Danish kitchen middens), the animals listed by Lubbock indicated climates more extreme than today. As present knowledge of fluctuating hot and cold, glacial and interglacial, were not known to Lubbock, he was puzzled by the mixture of evidence. His list is still useful even if the crucial indicators, the two kinds of elephant and rhinoceros, now have different specific names.

Chapters 10 and 11 are divided on the source of evidence: 'Cave Men' and 'River Drift Gravel Beds', and there is no doubt that at the time he had them in the right order, cave men later and so first. We miss the cultural terms used today, derived from the name of the place where they were first identified, but the upper Palaeolithic and lower Palaeolithic which roughly correspond are recognisable, the middle Palaeolithic still awaiting recognition.

After describing earlier cave excavations, particularly Brixham, we are introduced to Edouard Lartet, who had created a sequence based on the fauna, and so to the Dordogne and his excavations on the ten famous rock shelters, the work being financed by Henry Christy.[8] Lubbock said of these rock shelters, 'most of which I myself had the advantage of visiting'. There is unfortunately little illustration of the flint industry or blade tools, but a fine Mousterian scraper from Lubbock's own collection is shown from different angles (p. 320). We are shown the first art, engraved or carved bone with representations of animals (pp. 324–5). Rock paintings were still a subject for later editions.

The Neanderthal skull, the only one with clear deviation from modern skulls, had already been published by Lyell and Huxley but was illustrated here (p. 329). It has massive eye ridges, now known to be Mousterian or middle Palaeolithic in date (see this volume, frontispiece). The absence of early human fossil remains was one of the great difficulties for students of early man at this date.

Chapter 11 has one of the most striking opening paragraphs in the book:

> While we have been straining our eyes to the East and eagerly watching excavations in Egypt and Assyria suddenly a new light has arisen in the midst of us: and the oldest relics of man yet discovered have occurred not among the ruins of Nineveh or Heliopolis, not on the sandy plains of the Nile or Euphrates but in the pleasant valleys of England and France, along the banks of the Seine and the Somme, the Thames and Waveney.

Lubbock discussed only discoveries of hand-axes, especially by Boucher de Perthes in the Somme valley gravel pits (fig. 3) up to their formal authentication by Prestwich's lecture to the Royal Society in 1859.[9] It must be remembered that even in 1865 a great part of the educated classes, let alone the uneducated ones, knew nothing of the background and evidence from the gravels, unless they had read Lyell's *Antiquity of Man*, so Lubbock uses simple and direct language. To grasp that a river can carve out its valley and then fill it again, leaving deposits of gravel on the way down, takes some swallowing even today. Hand-axes, we are told, have been found in Spain and even India (the great discoveries in Africa had not occurred), for Lubbock, as we have said, thought in World terms.

Throughout the book French sources are left in French, and naturally in this chapter most sources are French. In Victorian times French and German were the languages of scientists, and so educated people were expected to read French at least; it provides an indication of the readership at which the book was directed. Today the publisher would be alarmed by the loss of sales caused by such a practice.

Chapter 12, entitled the 'Antiquity of Man', deals with attempts to propose real dates, and nowhere does it demonstrate more the great advances in this field since it was written, as we can see by the exact dating given in *The Human Past* edited by Scarre, more or less for the world over. Rates of deposition or the changes of the earth's eccentricity of orbit are not reliable guides.[10]

This concludes the archaeology in the book and leaves only the three chapters on 'modern savages' and 'concluding remarks'.

The chapters on modern primitives have been already discussed (p.23–24). They constitute the most original feature of the book. Once you go outside western Europe the subjects of ethnology or anthropology and prehistoric archaeology become intertwined, particularly in areas where there is no written history. Lubbock and the leading prehistorians (Evans, Pitt-Rivers, Franks) belonged to the Ethnological Society which covered both and combined in 1870 with the older Anthropological Society to form the Anthropological Institute, with Lubbock as its President. For a biologist who was used to living things, ethnology had its attraction over the mute flints, and as we have seen, Darwin turned to these chapters first.

The archaeology of Lubbock had been based on visiting sites and museums, often with the excavator or a geologist (except, significantly, the chapter on American archaeology). But whilst the ethnology was based on collections of material culture, it is true, it was mainly from reports from travellers, colonial administrators and missionaries thus was secondhand, deriving from not necessarily reliable sources by people for whom it was a secondary interest.

The first chapter deals with the primitives of the Old World: South Africa, south-east Asia, Australia, Oceania. The second deals with the two Americas, starting in the north with the Eskimos and ending in the extreme south with the Fuegans. The subjects briefly discussed are what could be culled from the literature or from collections, not only material culture but 'manners and customs', while the third chapter is more overtly anthropological, comparing weapons (p. 543) or general material culture (p. 541) or more specifically anthropological; the question of descent (p. 549).

The question that must arise is, do the three chapters enhance our understanding of the archaeology of the book? The answer is unquestionably yes. They bring us down to earth, for most of us have great difficulty in envisaging life in prehistoric times, so utterly divorced from modern life; the primitives faced much the same problems as the prehistoric peoples and took similar courses for survival. Of course they are not identical but they help to give reality to the prehistoric material culture.

The 'Concluding Remarks' are reproduced in Appendix 5. It was this chapter in the first edition that Darwin thought so highly of that he wondered why Lubbock wanted to leave science for politics (he stood unsuccessfully for West Kent in 1865) – 'Oh Dear, Oh dear, Oh dear'. It has several aspects: a defence and justification of 'Natural Selection' to which Man was apparently no longer subject: science was about to introduce a sort of Utopia; the dark cloud of sin still hung over us but might be dissipated by science. It is worth running through the main points to understand the later essays on 'happiness' (Appendix 7).

Lubbock held that the simple tools and devices have been independently invented by various tribes in different parts of the world. These would include stone tools, pottery, fire-making, houses (by copying

wild animals). He quoted E. B. Tylor, the anthropologist, that primitives never gave up any advance made. What had been the starting
point for man – the minimum below the existing primitives? Once
the first men left the abundance of the tropics they would have to get
their own food.

The unity of mankind implies that the division into races took
place very soon after man's origin. Wallace stated that there are two
schools of thought: man is a single species or he belongs to a genus
of several species. Wallace favoured the first. The solution is in natural selection, to which he was subject so long as he was an animal, but
once he emerged he was no longer bound by it. Lubbock did not favour
slow and gradual change; it still took place to produce races.

He is indeed a being apart since he is not influenced by the great
laws which irresistibly modify all organic beings.

> Thus the great principle of Natural Selection which is to
> biology what the law of gravitation is for astronomy not
> only throws an unexpected light on the past ... which
> thus teaches us humility for the past, faith in the present
> and hope for the future ... should have been regarded as
> opposed to the principles of Christianity or the interests
> of true religion. (pp. 580–81)

Lubbock had a devout boyhood (p.9) and here is trying to reconcile his
biology with his religion.

Now we come to happiness, which he believed was greatly on the
increase. A little crudely, this was implied by increasing numbers of
population which must imply conditions are more 'favourable'. This
is very much a biologist's argument. There follow some very interesting figures on the area of land required to support modern people of
this kind, and the very variable game in different habitats. Population
increases with civilisation.

Some doubt whether happiness is increased by civilisation, and
believe in the 'free and noble savage'. But the true savage is neither
free nor noble, he is a slave to his own wants, his own passions (p. 583).
Self-mutilation is another characteristic of savage life.

Looking at the bright side, 'As we descend in the scale of organisation animals do become more and more vegetative in their characteristics, with less susceptibility to pain and consequently less capacity for happiness' (p. 585). Happiness is at least partly feeling pain, for no consciousness of enjoyment or even existence is to be like a tree or seaweed.

'How much misery, for instance, has been spared the human race by the single discovery of chloroform?' (p. 587). Science will lead to a great improvement in the condition of man. Our sufferings and sorrows are due to *sin* however much science may ameliorate the situation. 'This separation of the two mighty agents of improvement ... has done more than anything else to retard the progress of civilisation'. 'Science may not make us more virtuous but at least it certainly makes us more innocent' (p. 587).

> Out of 130,000 persons committed to prison in England and Wales in 1867 only 4,137 could read and write well. In fact our prison population are mere savages. ... Most of our suffering arises from a mistaken pursuit of pleasure from a misapprehension of that which constitutes true happiness. (p. 588)

Science will soon come to the rescue by extending our understanding.

We are only on the 'threshold of civilisation, and tendency to improve proceeds with augmented impetus' (p. 589). Man has surely not reached the limits of his intellectual development, and it is certain he has not exhausted the infinite capabilities of nature. We may say like Newton that we are children on the beach picking up smooth pebbles and shells while the great ocean lies all undiscovered before us.

> The great principle of natural selection which in animals affects the body and seems to have little influence on the mind, in man affects the mind and has little influence on the body. ... Utopia which we long looked upon as impossibility ... turns out on the contrary to be a necessary consequence of natural laws, and once more we find that the simple truth exceeds the most brilliant flights of imagination ... (p. 590)

Lubbock reveals his own simple, if a little crude, philosophy, a highly optimistic one. He acknowledges his debt to Herbert Spencer. The relentless course of 'natural selection' will lead to a golden future because the past (described in the book) can only continue in the present and the future as it has before. He followed the optimistic line of Spencer, not of Darwin who had a more detached view; the adaptation caused by natural selection might be an improvement but could be a disaster, almost by definition, in the long run. The optimism is surely the parent of the Edwardian *belle epoque*, of H. G. Wells, that ended so disastrously in 1914.

Lubbock writes as a biologist but there is the dark shadow of *sin*, clearly deriving from his devout boyhood. In 1865 he was only 31 and *Prehistoric Times* was his first book. The distinction between 'pleasure' and 'happiness', the first not to be pursued and the second coming as a sort of by-product of work, is a very Victorian sentiment and again no doubt has a religious foundation.

Notes:

1. John Evans, 1872 and 1881
2. Daniel Wilson, 1851
3. V. G. Childe, five editions from 1925, recalling Lubbock's seven editions.
4. M. W. Thompson, 1953 with J. G. D. Clark, 1954. See also page 425 in this book for harpoons used by Andaman Islanders against pigs.
5. H. G. Hutchinson, 1914, vol. 1, p. 138 ff.
6. M. W. Thompson, see my PhD thesis (1953) in Cambridge University Library.
7. C. Scarre (ed.), 2005
8. E. Lartet and H. Christy, 1870
9. J. Prestwich, 1859
10. C. Scarre (ed.), 2005

4. *The Origin of Civilisation*

Before discussing the contents of the book giving its title to this chapter, we may say that it was a commercial success, six editions being published between 1870 and 1902, with a sort of final shot in 1911 entitled *Marriage, Totenism and Religion* published then.[1] *Prehistoric Times*, published first in 1865, had seven editions to 1913, the last only appearing after Lubbock's death. The latter was a larger book with sixteen chapters and 228 figures from the second edition. Except for a second edition, almost a reprint, in 1870, the *Origin* only had 20 figures throughout its life and a frontispiece unaltered after the second edition. The latter only had the study of secondary sources as its basis while *Prehistoric Times* was written after five years of travel to sites and museums. As a biologist, Lubbock was more at home with the relics of fossil man and the associated fauna than with the rather theoretical nature of anthropological studies. How did it come about?

The title page of the first edition gives the plain title of *Mental and Social Conditions of Savages*; we have already seen that he was very involved with primitives ('savages'), so this time their 'manners and cus-toms' are to be the main object of study, not just a supporting role. An Anthropological Society had existed since 1850, from which a breaka-way party had formed an Ethnological Society of which Lubbock was an extremely active member. This society received papers both on pre-historic archaeological and ethnological subjects, on the assumption that the two could not really be separated. As we have seen, in 1870 the two societies combined to form the Anthropological Institute of which Lubbock was the first President.

The word 'culture' is used today in normal conversation so we should understand its meaning. Any non-physical practice, which may of course manifest itself physically, passed on by each genera-tion, is culture: like marriage, language, religion, myth, song, dance, the skill in crafts such as pottery, metalwork etc. Used in this sense the word was a German invention. Gustav Lemm published 10 volumes of *Culturgeschichte* (Culture History) in 1843–5.[2] The culture of ten areas was described in the individual volumes. Although much of the material described is physical, such as boats or houses, it is the skill or habit that forms the culture, not the objects themselves, just as in pre-historic archaeology it is similar objects in an area that will or should denote a similar culture.

To judge by the advertisement, in 1855 Klemm was going to produce five volumes of 'Culturwissenschaft' (Culture Science or Anthropology), although only volume 2 as an introductory volume appeared, dealing with fire, food, drink and narcotics taken as individual traits, not as regional groups. This is what E. B. Tylor, who had been in Germany, was doing in 1865 in *Researches into the early History of Mankind and the Development of Civilisation*, and even Lubbock in 1870, who perhaps borrowed his title from Tylor. Sir Edward Burnet Tylor (1832–1917), the famous anthropologist, published his classic *Primitive Culture* in 1871. Both make acknowledgement to Klemm. A culture is defined by a group of similar traits, but it is the study of a single trait in different cultures that concerns us here; there is an analogy with the typology of single traits of Pitt-Rivers in material culture.

What distinguishes Lubbock's approach in this as in the last chapter is the world-wide scope of his knowledge, albeit of course at second-hand from publications. He has a preconceived idea of the line of development, and the countless examples are slotted in to fit this; there is of course no criticism of this. The thinking behind the book is that the primitives were people left behind after the original dispersal of one-type of man at his appearance. They were at various points along the road and by selecting the right examples we should be able to recover the line of the social progress of humanity. There is not a little of evolutionary theory in the mode of thought, perhaps more with Lubbock than Tylor. The point to which the path was pursued was 'civilisation', more or less literacy, and beyond this point they were no longer 'savages' or primitives. Both Tylor[3] and Lubbock agreed that the large body of evidence available from the primitives could be used historically to supplement the archaeological knowledge already acquired, since the life of the primitives resembled that of the vanished Stone Age men.

Lubbock saw three purposes in the study:

> In the first place the conditions and habits of existing savages resemble in many respects, though not in all, those of our own ancestors in a period long gone by; in the second they illustrate most of what is passing among ourselves and we can even penetrate some of the mystery which separates the present from the future ... (p. 1)

I doubt if Lubbock's optimism in the third sentence was shared by Tylor, the implication being that the past gave us grounds for predicting the future.

Lubbock lists the many possible sources of error from relying on reports from missionaries, civil servants, merchants, scientists from other fields, sailors, and so on, of which he was very conscious. Two inexplicable features puzzled him: the widespread feature of a woman not being allowed to speak to her son-in-law, and practice of 'Couvade' where after the birth of a child the father, not the mother, takes to his bed as if he has borne the child. He gives examples. Another puzzle: 'that a person imbibes the characteristics of an animal which he ate, is very widely distributed' (p. 12). It is silly to us but not to children. We need not pursue these quirks among the primitives, which are no doubt to some extent given to whet our appetites, for the Victorian scientist was expected to make his readers wonder!

In chapter 2 (all chapter numbers refer to the first edition, 1870) the subject is 'art and ornament', preceded by a plate showing an engraved mammoth on mammoth bone from an upper Palaeolithic French cave deposit. So we link up with *Prehistoric Times*, for the earliest traces of art belong to the Stone Age (p.25). Lubbock compares this sort of naturalistic art to that of the Eskimos, and contrasts it with geometric Polynesian art. He attributes the differences in the art to race and not to the similar way of life produced by similar conditions, notably the frozen conditions of the last ice age. Ignoring this, we can speak of an artistic sense in a culture at this early period. We are then introduced to the art, or lack of it, among various primitives. This leads to picture-writing on the path of progress which the book is demonstrating. Some of the signs from India are particularly interesting. The point has been made.

The last part of the chapter deals with ornamentation of the body by perforation for insertion of pendants or sticks, by painting, and especially by tattooing. Since quite attractive designs are produced in New Zealand or Polynesia in these media, demonstrating a strongly developed artistic sense among these people, the point is well made. Lubbock does not mention beads and necklaces, and tattooing, well known from the archaeological sites, nor indeed rock paintings, although the latter were hardly known about at this date.

The next chapter, which deals with 'Marriage and Relationships', is twice the length, and further lengthened and split into separate chapters in subsequent editions. This chapter and the following three on 'Religion' form the real heart of the book. The vital matter of reproduction and the cultural elements associated with it became the core element in anthropology. Indeed many might say that the kinship systems arising from the different kinds of association between the two sexes for reproduction was the kernel of anthropology.

Marriage and the relationship of a child to its father and mother seem to be so natural and obvious that we are apt to look on them as aboriginal and general to the human race. This is very far from being the case. The lowest races have no institution of marriage; true love is almost unknown among them. (p. 50)

Such a state of affairs would have shocked a Victorian audience, but also no doubt fascinated them, as Lubbock was well aware. He goes on to describe numerous unstable and non-existent relationships between the sexes, and the very lowly position of women among Australian aborigines. There were no hard and fast rules.

Yet we shall find, I think, that a man was first regarded as merely related to his family; then to his mother but not to his father; then to his father but not to his mother and only at the last to his father and mother. (p. 52)

fig 10. 'Marriage by capture' illustrated from Australia, regarded by MacLennan as an early stage in marriage history (Lubbock, 1870, pl. 3)

This sequence Lubbock sets out to demonstrate, but it would be tedious to recite his examples, some of which on closer study have proved to be wrong. They are indeed fascinating. His account suggests there really was no form of marriage, however transient it might be. 'Polyandry or the marriage of one woman to several men at once is more common than is generally supposed' (p. 55). There were lax and strict marriages, the latter being strict while they lasted. There might be some degree of violence involved (p. 59). The authority on primitive marriage, MacLennan,[4] identified 'marriage by capture' as a definite stage, also introduced the terms 'endogamy', meaning marriage within the clan, and 'exogamy', marriage outside the clan. Connected with the form of marriage were the kinship systems it served. 'Hetaerism' or communal marriage was the basis from which it started, at least theoretically, because no primitives could be found who practised it. The unit of 'consanguinity', to use Lewis Morgan's[5] term derived from his study of the Iroquois in North America, was the clan which was held together by such kinship systems. There was great interest in how units based on blood relationships could unite into the larger units of tribe, and in North America into nations.

Lubbock was much concerned with kinship systems, which form a very marked feature of later editions. We first meet it in this edition linguistically (p. 65) when the Hawaiian terms for relationship are given with the multiple English equivalents for the single Hawaiian term that might cover eight or ten English equivalents, so the former is much more economical than the latter. It is not necessary to pursue the matter here for the subject only appeals to some; in the British Library among the Lubbock papers is a sheet showing Gladstone's attempt to put his relatives into such a table.

Theoretically, after the free-for-all of hetaerism or communal marriage, there followed female supremacy followed by male supremacy.[6] Lubbock did not believe in the second stage, because of the lack of examples, and thought that exogamy prevailed, and he gives reasons for this. There is widespread evidence for wife-capture in different parts of the world, and Lubbock attributes the lowly position of women among primitives to this (fig. 10).

Modern opinion would doubt that communal marriage ever existed, but for Lubbock exogamy was required because of the unhealthy effects of inbreeding, no doubt a view taken over from MacLennan (p. 94), although he disagreed with him about the prevalence of 'endogamy' (p. 100). Lubbock explains descent through the female line on account of the close bond between mother and child: among primitives men's heirs are often his sister's children. The chapter concludes:

> ... the natural progress of ideas is first that a child is related to his tribe generally, secondly to his mother and not his father; thirdly to his father and not his mother; lastly and lastly only that he is related to both.

The next chapters, 4, 5 and 6, are devoted to religion and because, as we know, he still had religious feelings from his devout boyhood, the subject had a personal interest for him. He apologised to his readers for any repugnance they might feel about what he described (p. 114):

> I have felt doubtful whether this chapter should be called "the superstitions" rather than the religion of savages, but have preferred the latter, partly because many superstitious ideas pass gradually into nobler conceptions. ... We regard the Deity as good; they look upon him as evil; we submit ourselves to him; they endeavour to obtain control over him.
>
> There is no uniformity *tot homines quot sententiae*. (p.117)

Lubbock gives us seven stages: atheism (no definite ideas), fetishism (man tries to control deity), nature-worship or totemism (natural objects worshipped), shamanism (deities more powerful than man), idolatry or anthropomorphism (gods take the shape of men), God as author of nature not part of it, and a final stage when morality is associated with religion (p.119).

Although primitives with no religion have been reported, if religion is defined as belief in something more powerful than man, some sort of religion was probably universal. Lubbock gives examples of people who apparently had no religion. Dreams had an importance in lower forms of religion. Today of course our ideas about dreams usually have a Freudian origin, although some of us still share our belief in ghosts with our ancestors! Spirits were evil beings and regarded like a stranger from an alien tribe (p. 129). Death itself is regarded as unnatural and caused by sorcery or witchcraft (p.133). Spirits are not necessarily more powerful than men but more mischievous.

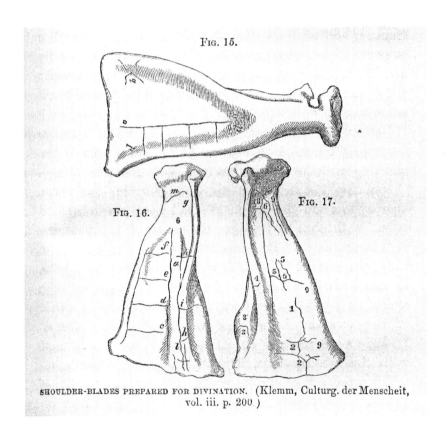

SHOULDER-BLADES PREPARED FOR DIVINATION. (Klemm, Culturg. der Menscheit, vol. iii. p. 200.)

fig 11. Shoulder blades marked for divination purposes (Lubbock, 1870, figs. 15–17)

No belief in a future life meant the grave ended everything (p.139). This view of Lubbock can hardly be reconciled with archaeological evidence from graves of provision for future life. There may be a belief in a spirit separate from the body but it only has a short life. Divination took various forms: by the cracks produced on shoulder bones after heating, dice throwing, black magic, confusion between name and person, witchcraft and sorcery, dance (p.155). Among savages it is no mere amusement. There were many occasions, such as war, when a dance was required.

Further steps followed in the gradual evolution of religious beliefs (p.158). Australians feared witchcraft as they had no notion of creation, nor did they say prayers as a deity would require them to do. After death a savage became a white person. Fetishism developed among negroes (p.164). By means of the fetish the deity can be coerced or controlled. Part of an enemy could serve as the fetish. We are dealing with a form of witchcraft. In totemism (p.169), any natural thing could be worshipped: trees, stones, rivers, heavenly bodies, animals, plants and so on; after the adoption of the name of an animal the living subject would be treated with awe. For Lubbock the use of the name of an animal became a totem more or less accidentally, since it came to be regarded with awe. He cited the 'kobong' in Australia to illustrate this. Fergusson[7] had published a book about the very widespread worship of trees and serpents (p. 177). The housing necessary for such an animal created, in effect, a temple.

Animal worship was very prevalent in America, in Mexico and Peru. Polynesians had almost passed beyond this stage and become semi-civilised (p.181). Primitives regard their deity as a part of nature (p. 188), for they account all movement as life, even in some cases the wind. There is widespread worship of trees, like the bo tree in India and Ceylon, where also there is a divinity in water and rivers like the Ganges. There was widespread worship of upright stones, often quite indiscriminately. Plate 2 shows painted upright stones at Delgaum in the Deccan, the frontispiece in volume 1, painted with a red blob thought to signify blood. The great stone at Mecca is also mentioned. Fire and the sun are widely worshipped (p. 215).

There are two different kinds of modification: *developmental*, due to intellectual progress, a more elevated idea of the Deity, while *adaptational* might well be due to climate in hot or cold parts of the globe (p. 219). Language has influenced development: Aryan languages are associated with complicated mythology while Semitic languages have gods of a different kind: Baal, Adonis (land), Sket (master), Moloch (king) compared to Zeus (sky), Phoebus Apollo (sun), Neptune (sea) etc. The more unpleasant parts of Classical myths can be explained allegorically (p. 223).

'The worship of idols characterises a somewhat higher stage of human development' (p.225). Idols and fetishes can be confused, but the earlier are an attack on the deity, while idolatry is worship of him; the two are opposites. Idols are unknown to the Eskimo, and in West Africa fetishes have been mistaken for idols:

> it can be laid down as a constant rule that mankind arrives at the stage of monarchy in government before he reaches idolatry in religion. The idol usually assumes the human form and idolatry is closely connected with the form of religion which consists of the worship of ancestors. (p.228)

Lubbock says it is 'no part of my plan to describe the religious beliefs of the higher races' although he does introduce their beginnings, telling us of sacrifices of animals where the dead animal is eaten, so passing on its spirit to the eater. Many cases of human sacrifice are mentioned, which presumably with Central American practices in mind he regards as possible for the higher races to practise. 'Without temples and sacrifices there can be no priests' (p. 245). Wizards are often mistaken for priests. A future state is believed in as future life, and killing of older people gives them entry into it. Creation stories are emerging but prayer comes later.

Morality is only possible when it is associated with religion:

> The time however is approaching when it will be generally perceived that science so far from being opposed to religion, true religion is, without science, impossible. (p. 256)

In chapter 7 we enter a very different field: character and morals of the primitives; it is a difficult subject because of the conflicting and quite often unreliable accounts available. It is difficult to judge an individual, let alone a group. Wallace is quoted on the idealised condition he found among smaller communities in south-east Asia, on which Lubbock remarked:

> But does this prove that they are in a high moral condition? Does it prove that they have any moral sense at all? Surely not. For if it does we must equally credit rooks and bees, and most other gregarious animals, with a moral state higher than that of civilised man. (p. 263)

He goes on to say that family feeling, like a mother's affection for her children, must not be confused with the moral condition of savages, which is really much lower than has been generally supposed. He then quotes many reports that bear this out.

The character of the Greek gods is familiar to us and was anything but moral. Such Beings would certainly not reward the good, or punish evil. Hence it is not surprising that Socrates saw little connection between ethics and religion, or that Aristotle altogether separated morality from theology ... (p. 266)

Lubbock's Victorian views on morality are not in tune with modern views, and while we should be aware of them they cannot be followed at length.

Lubbock quotes Herbert Spencer: 'Moral intuitions are the results of accumulated experiences of utility; gradually organised and inherited, they have come to be quite independent of conscious experience' (p. 270). Needless to say, Lubbock did not agree, 'for in our own case religion and morality are closely connected together' (p. 273):

> Yet the sacred character, which forms an integral part in our conception of duty, could not arise until Religion became sacred. Nor would take place until the Deities were conceived to be beneficent beings. As soon as this happened, however, they would naturally be supposed to

regard with approbation all that tended to benefit their worshippers, and to condemn all actions of the opposite character. This step was an immense benefit to mankind … Authority, then, seems to me the origin, and utility though not in the manner suggested by Mr Spencer, the criterion of virtue … (p. 273)

Language is the subject of the next chapter, for it is known to all primitives, although where there are a great number of mutually unintelligible languages there are advantages in using the sign language described by Tylor. This is particularly the case among American Indians.

The origin of language is discussed, and the problems caused by the absence of the verb 'to be' in the North American languages. The great authority of the period, Max Müller, who worked in England, cited the very small vocabulary of an agricultural labourer of 300 words as indicating that only a small number of words were needed to explain the origin of language, since only a small number of words were required to set the ball rolling. The author goes into great detail on the root words. The subject is fascinating, although modern opinion would not regard the problem as resolved even by this ingenious explanation.

There are long lists of the terms for mother and father in most parts of the world, which gives rise to discussion of the root in either case. The root of pa or ba is world-wide for baby and father. The roots exist 'as Plato would say, by nature … when we say by nature we mean by the hand of God' (p. 290). He goes on to show the inadequacies of the languages of many primitives:

Thus the Choclaw language has names for the black oak, white oak and red oak, but none for an oak; still less for a tree. … The Tasmanians could not express qualities such as hard, soft, warm, cold, long, short, round. (p. 292)

Other difficulties, particularly of counting above two or four, are described. Lubbock does not venture to describe the origin of grammar!

These examples appear to me very instructive; we seem as it were to trace up the formation of the numerals; we perceive the true cause of the decimal system of notation; and we obtain interesting if melancholy evidence of the extent to which the faculty of thought lies dormant among the lower races of man. (p. 299)

In chapter 9 the subject is law, for 'The progress and development of law is indeed one of the most interesting as well as most important sections of human history' (p. 300). Lubbock quotes Goguet as mistakenly seeing monarchical government as the earliest and most universal form of government for lack of studying the primitives. The laws of Australian aborigines must have been not for a single family but for groups together.

Even Maine[8] in his excellent work failed to study primitives for 'the lowest races of savages have laws' (p. 300):

Nay, every action of their lives is regulated by numerous rules, nonetheless stronger for being unwritten. ... they are governed by a code of rules and a set of customs which form one of the most cruel tyrannies that has ever, perhaps, existed on the face of the earth. ... This is no peculiar case. No savage is free. All over the world his daily life is regulated by a complicated and apparently most inconvenient set of customs enforceable as law ... the prohibitions as a general rule apply to the women and the privileges to the men ... (p. 303)

Hunting tribes have rules well understood with reference to game. This is particularly the case where more than one attempt has been made on the game but has failed to bring it down, on the question of who gets the animal when finally killed.

A high degree of protocol obtains in salutations, ceremonies and festivals among primitives. Examples are given from Australia and Tonga, where the third person is used (p. 306). In the absence of writing, witnesses are essential, with a strong impression being made on their minds.

Property makes laws of inheritance essential. Contrast, for example, the North American Indians who held land communally, as in the Russian *mir*, with the Australians where each male had a holding. Treatment of land as a commercial commodity is a relatively recent state of affairs, and wills as a legal process even more recent (pp. 309–11).

Maine is quoted on wills with recognisable features: 1) takes effect on death, 2) can be secret, 3) revocable. Roman law acquired these characteristics very slowly. Wills are unknown among most primitives, for in Australia the land is divested during lifetime. Crime was regarded as a personal matter between victim and aggressor in which society played no part, and was normally settled by 'payment' (Latin *pagare*). Roman law had *culpa* payment related to the degree of blame.

In his general conclusions (pp. 322–5) Lubbock concedes that some nations have 'retrogressed', but this is due to exceptional circumstances; existing savages are not the descendants of civilised societies. The primitive condition of man was one of 'utter barbarism' and from this several nations have independently raised themselves.

> These views follow, I think, from strictly scientific considerations. We shall not be the less inclined to adopt them on account of the cheering prospects which they hold out for the future. In the closing chapter of *Prehistoric Times* while fully admitting the charms of savage life I have endeavoured to point out the immense advantages we enjoy. Here I will only add that if the past history of man has been one of deterioration, we have but a groundless expectation for future improvement; on the other hand if the past has been one of progress we may fairly hope that the future will be also; that the blessings of civilisation will not only be extended to other countries and to other nations, but that even in our own time they will be rendered more general and more equable; so that we shall not see before us always, as now, countrymen of our own living in our very midst a life worse than that of a savage; neither enjoying the rough advantages and real though coarse pleasures of savage life nor yet availing themselves

of the far higher and more noble opportunities which lie within the reach of civilised Man (p. 323).

Lubbock was elected to Parliament in the same year as a Liberal with the intention of various improvements, and one feels an element of the political speech has come in here.

The book concludes with two papers that Lubbock gave to summer meetings of the British Association for the Advancement of Science at Dundee (p. 325) and Exeter in 1869 (p. 337). In the first case it was to answer criticism from the Archbishop of Dublin, and in the second criticism from the Duke of Argyll. The question was whether man at his first appearance was in a state of savagery from which some had risen, or he had been civilised and the primitives had deteriorated to their present state. From what has been said above we can understand the strong argument by Lubbock for the former case, and it is not necessary to follow the argument.

Lubbock at the end of his life wrote a book entitled *Marriage, Totemism and Religion: an answer to critics*, 1911. The title shows its purpose and we might indeed expect that after there would be criticism. In fairness they were not very fundamental and we need not enter into the details of his answers to his critics.

Notes:
1. Lubbock, 1911
2. G. Klemm, 1843–5 and 1855
3. E. Tylor, 1865
4. J. MacLennan, 1865
5. B. Stern, 1931
6. J. Bachofen, 1841
7. J. Fergusson, 1868
8. H. Maine, 1861

5. Return to Biology

The title of this chapter is quite misleading: for Lubbock, from his time of youthful self-education onwards, biology was his love, which as a pupil of Darwin we might reasonably expect to be the case. The two books on prehistoric archaeology and anthropology ran into later editions, and apart from *Marriage and Totemism*, an answer to criticism near the end of his life, he did not return to those fields. The list of his books in Appendix 1 demonstrates this point.

Lubbock's excellent little book *On the Origin and Metamorphosis of Insects*, published in 1873, shortly after the two editions of *The Origin of Civilisation*, lists 35 papers published between 1853 and 1872 on biological subjects. There is no break in the flow in 1865–70 when the two books on archaeology and anthropology were published. Articles for scientists usually record original work, while books are often summaries, so there is no question of him not doing original work.

In the two issues of the book on his life-work edited by his daughter (published in 1924, reprinted 1934) the chapters are written by experts in the different fields: four of the ten chapters (five if we include 'Anthropology') are by scientists and constitute just under or just over half the full text. He regarded himself as primarily a scientist, a biologist. The contributors divide his science into 'Geology' (Smith Woodward FRS), 'Zoology' (Professor J. A. Thomson), 'Entomology' (H. Donisthorpe FRS) and Botany (Dr Seward FRS). No doubt these assessments of 1924 are out of date for they were written eleven years after Lubbock's death, but they are the best we have; reputations are short-lived, especially in science. In this chapter a chronological rather than a subject division will be followed.

Darwin referred to himself as a 'naturalist', as did Lubbock, although increasingly he spoke of 'science', 'Scientific lectures', 'Fifty Years of Science'. The British Association for the Advancement of Science, founded in 1831 with its various sections, met in different cities every summer and was regularly attended by Lubbock and colleagues. The creation of new societies by those with special interests made it difficult to use a broad term like *naturalist*. Lubbock was an active member, often becoming President, as for instance with the Entomological Society. Nevertheless there were factors that acted in favour of prolonging the life of the naturalist until he was swallowed up by the laboratory at the end of the century.

The naturalist was essentially a 'loner' working from his home, with his finances derived from inherited wealth supplemented by a business, like a bank in Lubbock's case or a paper factory in the case of John Evans. The naturalist without resources, like Huxley, had to seek appointments with an institution like a university or museum, and in Huxley's case his friends had to rally round. Darwin, Lubbock, Lyell and others could earn significant, even substantial, sums from their publications.

Although the naturalist might travel for experience in his youth, like Darwin, Wallace and Christy, it was a profession that largely worked from home, where they may have lived with a large family like Darwin or Lubbock did. They had an active social life with their colleagues in the London clubs, especially the Athenaeum, the societies, particularly the Royal Society, and the annual summer meetings of the British Association for the Advancement of Science (BAAS). They might travel together; Lubbock was accompanied by Busk or Evans or Prestwich in his trips to the Somme or Scandinavia. The rather secluded life led by Darwin, who shunned societies, is in very marked contrast to the very convivial life led by Lubbock.

Among the different dining clubs to which Lubbock belonged, two throw some light on his views.[1] The X Club, founded in 1864, never had more than nine members, the original ones, who met monthly to dine and probably to discuss matters concerned with the Royal Society, of which all were Fellows except Herbert Spencer, the scientific philosopher. Members included Busk, Hooker, Huxley, Spencer and Tyndall. It had two mathematicians and two philosophers besides the 'naturalists', who were indeed becoming rather specialised. It had 270 meetings and the average attendance in the early years was seven. Spencer gives some insight into its workings in his fascinating *Autobiography*, although he was by no means a typical member. Most members achieved distinction in various ways, three being Presidents of the Royal Society. It was clearly an influential group in the scientific world.

The other club or society could hardly be of greater contrast. It was called the Metaphysical Society, founded a little later in 1869. The Archbishop of York, several bishops and deans gave it a decidedly clerical flavour. However its secular members included Gladstone and literary celebrities like Tennyson and Ruskin.

After much hesitation Huxley was invited to join and he took an active part in the discussions. Although called a society, they dined first, with their discussion afterwards. According to Lubbock the differences of opinion between the High and Low Church of England and Non-Conformists went so deep on the question of a President that he, as a safe outsider, was invited to fill the post. The nature of the society, from the top level, not only reveals the people with whom Lubbock mixed (Gladstone was a personal friend entertained at High Elms) but also his continuous if slightly vaporous religious belief. One remembers his ability to persuade the Dean to allow Darwin's ceremonial burial in Westminster Abbey in 1882, where he himself was a pall bearer. He forwarded a petition from a group of MPs.

The way the naturalists worked from home had a considerable influence on the nature of the work they did. There was no laboratory, no test tubes or Bunsen burners, and instead a study or library served, where the microscope, the chief badge or instrument of the naturalist, was housed. The size of Victorian houses and the donkey work done by servants made this adaptation fairly easy to achieve. No white coat was needed to work under these comfortable conditions.

We have seen how Darwin supplied a microscope for Lubbock while still a boy and how his youthful self-education schedule showed that work with the microscope was its most important element. Indeed it is probable that so much of his work with insects, small invertebrates, and the leaf and flower structure of plants was possible because drawings could be done from magnified images on the slides of the microscope. This did not require elaborate apparatus for chemical or physical treatment. No computers were needed. Typewriters were not in general use until towards the end of the century and I am not sure that suitable photography was in use much earlier.

MODE OF OBSERVATION. 3

observation. I found it convenient to have one side of the nest formed by a loose slip of wood, and at one corner I left a small door. These glass nests I either kept in shallow boxes with loose glass covers resting on baize, which admitted enough air, and yet was impervious to the ants; or on stands surrounded either by water, or by fur, with the hairs pointing downwards. Some of the nests I arranged on stands, as shown in

FIG. 1.

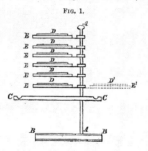

fig. 1. A A is an upright post fixed on a base B B. C C is a square platform of wood round which runs a ditch of water. Above are six nests, D, each lying on a platform E, which could be turned for facility of observation, as shown in the dotted lines D′ and E′. Thus the ants had a considerable range, as they could wander as far as the water ditch. The object of having the platform C C larger than the supports of the nests

B 2

fig 12. Artificial ants' nests at High Elms, surrounded by water. Glass plates were attached to a stand to assist inspection (Lubbock, 188, fig. 1)

Much of the naturalist's work had to be done by improvisation by using what was around him: one thinks of Darwin studying earthworms or indeed the experimental work described in the *Origin of Species*. It does not detract from the value of the work but gives it a domestic flavour, especially bearing in mind the style, a rather comradely one, very distant from today's science. In the case of Lubbock's *Ants, Bees and Wasps*, the classic instance of home science, he had his very ingeniously designed ants' nests of glass plates in his garden, allowing him to breed, keep and study the creatures (fig. 12). Was there any better way of studying their behaviour? The bees and wasps were more difficult and had to be based on simple observation. No wonder the book had 18 editions and was a common household need, because this form of science was so easily understandable or even reproducible.

In science as in music, the performer requires an appreciative audience beyond colleagues; we are fortunate that Chicago University Press has just brought out three books on popular science in the nineteenth century. O'Connor has shown the growth in popularity of earth science, geology, in the first half of the nineteenth century, started by the discovery of fossil monsters, first mammoth and then the huge reptiles of an earlier period.[2] Geology indeed replaced astronomy as the respectable science, and then thanks to Lyell achieved a pre-eminent position. Lubbock saw, as we have seen, the new science of prehistoric archaeology to be based on the methods of geology. Lyell had of course demonstrated the 'antiquity of man' geologically two years before Lubbock published his book. The extent of the broad base of the pyramid of interest in the middle and later nineteenth century has been revealed by Lightman and Fyfe.[3] The pyramid had fairly gently sloping sides, so the level reached where the means and education was available to buy and read Lubbock's books was a large one (quite apart from subscribing libraries). This helps explain the volume of his publications.

Another factor was the cheapening of printing caused by steam printing. It was apparently the publisher (Williams and Norgate) who suggested that Lubbock put together his accounts of his travels to form a book, which came out as *Prehistoric Times*. The diaries leave no doubt that he was under pressure from publishers to correct proofs of new editions. Hutchinson refers to a secretary and it is difficult to believe that Lubbock produced as much as he did without paid assistance.

Turning now to individual books, which are listed chronologically in Appendix 1, some but not all may be mentioned, bearing in mind that there was a very substantial publication of articles not treated here. Lubbock's third book, published in 1871 as a monograph of the Ray Society, was entitled *Monograph on the Collembola and Thysanura*. This forbidding title conceals one of Lubbock's most valuable books, something like his PhD thesis.

> Yet if a fallen bough be examined, a heap of moss shaken over a pocket handkerchief, or any long herbage swept with a hand net, the naturalist will not fail to find, together with numerous beetles, flies and other insects, certain delicate hexapod, active little creatures ... running with agility but also springing with considerable force ... These constitute the Linnaean genus *Podura* or Springtail ... to call *Collembola* [leaving] *Thysanura* for the other portion of the group. (p. 1)

We are dealing with a reclassification of Spring-tails and Bristle-tails into two separate orders by someone with a sound knowledge of the Continental work. On page 39 a table shows the two new Orders with six families for the *Collembola* and two for the *Thysanura*. It was then quite a major new classification, with many new genera, and to the best of my knowledge still obtains.

The book ends with 78 plates, some in colour, from specimens magnified by between 20 and 250 times. They illustrate the central part played by the microscope in the studies of the 'naturalist'. The latter word is used throughout. The coloured plates make it an attractive book. Published by a society only formed 25 years before, it is in no sense a popular work. The primitive character of these creatures, without wings or metamorphosis, led to discussion of the evolutionary origin of insects in general.

We have already referred to *The Origin and Metamorphosis of Insects* of 1873 as an important book with magnified drawings. This and the work on Spring-tails were essentially descriptive works, but by 1873

Lubbock had already started forming ants' nests in the garden at High Elms and so was now able to study the living creatures at first hand. This culminated in the famous *Ants, Bees and Wasps, a record of observation on the Hymenoptera*, 1882, where the record is mainly about the behaviour of ants, rather than the more elusive bees and wasps. In many ways this was the most original research he did, ably described by Professor J. Arthur Thomson and Mr J. K. Donisthorpe FRS in 1934.[5]

> It is no exaggeration to assert that all the numerous experiments on the psychology of ants devised and conducted in more recent times are based on his original researches.[6]

It must be left to experts to assess Lubbock's contributions to the study of animal behaviour, but the public was very appreciative of what became almost a household necessity to judge by the 18 editions it went through, the last in 1929 being Lubbock's only book to be reprinted after the war.

The other interest that arose from his study of living creatures, although not so much the ants as the bees and wasps, was their intimate relationship with plants: *British Wild Flowers in Relation to Insects*, 1874 and *On Certain Relations between Plants and Insects*, 1878. This gradual shift in interest from insects to plants was to turn Lubbock in the next decade into more of a botanist than a zoologist, as we shall see below.

However, before leaving insects there is a well-known passage from Lubbock that is worth quoting, even if none of us would agree with it and he was probably speaking rhetorically:

> The anthropoid apes no doubt approach nearer to man in bodily structure than do any other animals; but when we consider the habits of ants, their social organisation, their large communities and elaborate habitations; their roadways, their possession of domestic animals, and even in some cases of slaves, it must be admitted they have a fair claim to rank next to man in the scale of intelligence.[7]

It is the question of the use of the word 'intelligence' that is at issue. Victorians would have relished the paradox. We must leave this, and animal behaviour generally, to those properly qualified to speak about them, and pursue the matter of Lubbock as a botanist.

His books of 1874 and 1878 on the relationship of insects to plants have already been mentioned. The subject was one that interested Darwin, and this may have influenced Lubbock; it was the need for the nectar by insects and the accidental pollination of the plant with which he was primarily concerned. This developed into a full-blown study of plant parts in the 1880s, *Flowers, Fruit and Leaves*, 1886. After 1889 it had superseded the interest in animal behaviour, although study with the microscope still played a central role. We must refer the reader to Dr Seward's account in 1934 of Lubbock's botanical work. Whether *La Vie des Plantes*, 1889, is a translation (many translations of his work were published) or written anew by him I cannot say as I have not seen a copy; Lubbock was quite able to write in French.

There can be no omission of the two-volume work, *A Contribution to the Study of Seedlings*, 1892, which has some claim to being his most important contribution to the subject. It was a major work dedicated to Sir Joseph Hooker (a fellow member of the X Club), Director of Kew Gardens where we may suspect much of the research and writing was done. The two volumes contained 1,254 pages and 684 illustrations with a substantial bibliography, mainly of German works, for the subject had hardly been studied in England. It was essentially a specialist study (the pages had not been cut in the University Library copy!), and his most impressive work. Dr Seward commented in 1934:

> For botanists this book is the most useful and original of Lord Avebury's contributions to the science ... The value of Lord Avebury's volumes lies in the wealth of material described and admirably illustrated ... The work contains a more complete account of seedlings than any other work in the English language.

Written in 1934, it may still retain its value. Lubbock had considerable help in its production.

Lubbock's last botanical work was published in 1905, for already from the 1880s his publications were increasingly of essays and political works and geological guides; it is to these that attention must now be turned.

The 'naturalist' required some knowledge of geology both for the fossil record and its influence on the landscape, such as important features of surrounding nature. Comparing Lubbock's account of the Somme terraces with that of Lyell in the *Antiquity of Man*, with its different sections, there is an impression that at that time the former's knowledge of geology was not that strong. Geology was not in Lubbock's schedule for self-study, although he had some experience on the Thames gravels, but characteristically he had improved it for he published works on Swiss scenery in 1896 and England in 1902. Neither were works of research but more in the nature of geological guides, well-informed and certainly useful for the traveller not well-informed on local work.

The diaries show that Lubbock went with his family (he remarried in 1884) to Switzerland more or less every autumn from the 1880s, although he knew the country from the 1860s when he had been looking at lake dwellings. As he was especially concerned with glaciations during the Quaternary or Palaeolithic period, it was an extremely appropriate place to go to study the effects of contemporary and past glaciation. Dr Woodward in 1934 described the book he wrote as a 'useful handbook'. His only original contribution in this field was his experiments to demonstrate that the mountain ranges were created by lateral, not upward, pressure.[9]

I hope enough has been said to show that he was much more than a popular writer on science but within his restricted facilities devised ingenious experiments and pushed the boundaries of the subject further forward in several areas. He relished describing his work to the public without lowering standards; how many scientists can make a description of work on such an unpromising subjects as ants, bees and wasps into a household requirement? As a rich man and a banker and, more seriously, successful both with the public and his peers, he inevitably provoked envy, then and now. How much credit is given to his scientific work in the New DNB?

Notes:

1. Hutchinson, 1914, vol. 1, pp. 63–4; 101–102
2. O'Connor, 2008
3. Lightman, 2007; Fyfe and Lightman, 2007
4. O'Connor, 2008, chapter 1
5. Grant Duff, 1934, pp. 115–136 and 157–67
6. ibid., p. 157. For a hostile view see Clark, 1997
7. Grant Duff, 1934, pp. 131–132
8. ibid., pp. 186–7
9. ibid., p. 110

6. The Politician

Lubbock stood unsuccessfully for West Kent in 1865 and 1868, but was elected as the Liberal member for Maidstone in 1870. He held the seat successfully until 1880 when he lost it, but the resignation of the member for London University allowed him to return to Parliament very shortly afterwards. There he held the seat for 20 years until his elevation to the Lords where he remained until his death in 1913. His title of Lord Avebury referred of course to the famous Wiltshire earthwork with which he had been associated; he took the change in status very seriously and bought Kingsgate Castle, Kent (a Victorian 'folly' according to Pevsner of 1860) which he completed and made his main residence from then on, and where he died, but High Elms was still retained in use.

The first question that must come to mind is why did he wish to enter Parliament? His father tried to stop him but his death in 1865 meant his son inherited the baronetcy, the bank and High Elms, with a fortune that enabled Lubbock to be very much his own master. Not only his father but Darwin and Hooker were horrified that his scientific talents would be wasted in politics; in fact he quite successfully combined the two. Lubbock was very conscious of status, ambitious if you like, so a life of merely commuting from High Elms to the City was no doubt not a very attractive one. Not only status but the power to make things happen would be considerably enhanced in Parliament. Although we may doubt that he had any very clear idea of what he proposed to do, he had been very impressed by the protection given to the prehistoric monuments in Denmark.

Lubbock was a Liberal at the time of his election but his reforming activities were outside the parameters of party policies, although not of course in conflict with them. The relationship of the party to its members in the House of Commons was quite different to what it is today; it would be quite impossible for a private member now to introduce the volume of legislation that Lubbock did in the nineteenth century. He was a personal friend of Gladstone at least up to 1885 supporting Home Rule for Ireland; the ability of Lubbock to get his legislation through was certainly affected by whether the government in power was hostile or friendly to it. Thus his difficulties in 1874–80, when the Liberals were in opposition and the Government was indifferent or hostile, delayed the passage of his Ancient Monuments Bill.

Kingsgate Castle

fig 13. Kingsgate 'Castle', Kent, a Victorian structure acquired by Lubbock and where he lived from 1902 until his death in 1913 (Hutchinson, 1914, p. 132)

Although he continued with his private bills, really public bills, throughout his life, and the subject will be dealt with below, the major traumatic political event of his life was the upheaval caused by Gladstone's adherence to Home Rule for Ireland. Today we are very used to nationalistic movements and colonies becoming independent but it was quite alien in Victorian England, long after the American experience. Lubbock was well-informed on the Empire generally and Ireland was much closer to home.[2] The issue tore the Liberals apart, the opponents of Home Rule forming a separate party, National Liberals or Unionists.

The loss of his seat in 1880 made it impossible for Gladstone to offer him office, and the events following Gladstone's persistence over Home Rule finally stopped any hopes that he may have had of holding high office. Home Rule had other effects and was almost certainly the main stimulus to his great interest in 'proportional representation' leading to the book with that title published in 1884 and with later editions, at least six, up to 1906, and he was also very active in the Society promoting it. In the later editions he cited the 1886 general election, where there were 1,423,500 Unionist votes and 1,353,400 votes for Home Rule. This gave 394 Unionist members and 275 Home Rule members, whereas with proportional representation the figures would have been 349 Unionists and 320 Home Rulers. It certainly made the point, albeit hardly in Lubbock's favour!

The same subject led to a run of letters in *The Times* in 1887, collected together under the title of *Mr Gladstone and the Nationalities of the United Kingdom*. Lubbock thought Gladstone meant ethnic divisions when he said 'nationalities'.

Bryce from Scotland pointed out that the two were not the same thing; my impression is that Lubbock had the worst of the argument but we need not enter into details.

In later life Lubbock took on something of the role of elder statesman: his book on *Free Trade* of 1904 has eight chapters ranging over the benefits that it had brought to the United Kingdom and the evident disadvantages of *Protectionism*. The subject was an old one and a central one of the Liberals ever since they were founded. He gave interesting figures on trade and decided that the English lower class was better off than those in Germany, Russia and France.

He admits that the condition of the working class in England was terrible, and as Principal of the Working Mens' College in London he was in a position to know.[3] We may bear this in mind when considering his own legislation to which we now turn.

The large number of Bills with which Lubbock is associated, most of which became Acts, is listed in Appendix 4:[4] there are 30 items in the list dealing with the most varied subjects and so defy easy classification. The first question that one is bound to ask is why do the subjects dealt with in the Bills seem so trivial? It must be that a private member could really only hope to initiate legislation on non-controversial issues because major issues inevitably impinged on party policy and were not matters that the private member could bring forward. Some of his Bills in later times became major issues like hours of work as in the Shop Hours Regulation Act of 1886 or the Shop Hours Act of 1904, or Open Spaces Act of 1890, now a planning matter. Even the Bank Holiday Act of 1871, at a time when there were only religious holidays, has become a major issue. A number of Bills represent his own special interests, like the Falsification of Accounts Act of 1874, Wild Birds' Protection Act of 1880, Bankers' Book Evidence Act or indeed the Ancient Monuments Act of 1882.

In many ways his Bank Holiday Act was his main political achievement, so permanent in its long-term effect of introducing or perhaps legitimising secular holidays, brought in almost as soon as he was elected. It combined two of his special interests: banking and reducing the hours of work to zero on at least one day, in fact four days. Those who think that Lubbock never had an original thought might well ponder the background against which the measure was taken. It epitomises Lubbock's view that achievable amelioration not social revolution was the best way to help the working classes:

> 34 and 35 Victoria, chap. 17, p. 1, 25 May 1871
>
> 1. After the passing of this Act the several days in the schedule to this Act mentioned (and which days hereinafter referred to as bank holidays) shall be kept as close days in all banks in England and Ireland and Scotland respectively ... .

The schedule shows four bank holidays in England and Ireland: Easter Monday, Whit Monday, first Monday in August, and 26th December if a weekday. Scotland had as well New Year's Day. Clauses allowed Her Majesty 'to appoint a special day to be observed as a bank holiday'.

The Ancient Monuments Act of 1882 had a very chequered career as a Bill, but was to some extent an appendix to chapter 3 of his book, that is *Prehistoric Times*, and for that reason deserves much fuller treatment here. As we said, Lubbock had been very impressed by steps taken in Denmark to preserve the prehistoric monuments, more particularly the numerous megaliths. This may have stimulated him in 1861 or on his second trip – he spent five years looking at European monuments – to start on legislation as soon as he entered Parliament in 1870. Before following the Bill's bumpy course we may turn to two cases in the 1870s where he was involved in 'direct action'.

The first was the great circular earthwork with internal circles of upright stones which represents a large and very important religious monument of perhaps 3,000 BC, from which later he took his title of Lord Avebury. The President of the Wiltshire Archaeological Society, warned of a threat, approached Lubbock with a request to prevent development on the site. He intervened and bought part of the ground within the circle. Subsequently he bought the great artificial mound to the south, Silbury Hill, for £500.[6] The other case is Caesar's Camp, Wimbledon, an Iron Age or Roman earthwork enclosure levelled in 1877 but retained in the schedule of the Bill even after destruction. The owner who gave evidence admitted that he simply caused the bank to be shovelled into the ditch. This came up in a Parliamentary Committee held between 8th February and 14th August 1877 under the Chairmanship of Sir John Lubbock.[7]

These are two well-documented cases of damage intended or executed: Lubbock cites many more in his valuable article on his reasons for pursuing the question of protective legislation for ancient monuments.[8] We may well agree about the destruction that was taking place for he cited particularly the destruction of the stones at Avebury by heating the stones with fire and then throwing cold water on them.[9] But why were medieval monuments excluded from his purview?

But we are told that we ought to include medieval monuments. The examples dealt with in the Bill, however, differ from medieval monuments in only wanting to be left alone. No appreciable annual outlay would be required for their protection. Medieval monuments on the contrary require constant supervision and frequent repairs entailing large expenses.[10]

This is true and the argument would and did appeal to Government, but if the prehistoric monuments were 'best left alone' why legislate at all? We have argued elsewhere that Lubbock's real motive was that prehistoric monuments demonstrated the antiquity of man in evolutionary terms, as Darwin, Lubbock's teacher, had taught him.[11] The Schedule to the 1882 Act which lists the monuments to which the Act will apply is reproduced in Appendix 4 and shows prehistoric monuments, almost exclusively prehistoric in England and Wales, with some early Christian ones in Scotland and Ireland.

When studying the Bill in its changing forms from 1873 to 1882 two features deserve attention. The first was compulsory powers, the power to compulsorily purchase the monument if the owner intended to alter or destroy it, which Lubbock believed caused the resistance to the Bill in both Houses of Parliament. No doubt this is true for such powers were omitted from the Bill in the form drawn up by the Government that it took in 1882. It is clear that from the beginning the problem of who was to exercise the powers in the Bill was a difficult one. Only the elected Government had the moral authority to exercise such powers, as events demonstrated.

Lubbock wanted an independent commission which by 1877 had achieved the form he described in his article which would consist of:

> ... the Enclosure Commissioners, the Master of the Rolls, the President of the Society of Antiquaries of London, the President of the Society Antiquaries of Scotland, the President of the Royal Irish Academy, Keeper of British Antiquities at the British Museum ...

There were also seven nominated Commissioners including 'the Duke of Devonshire. ... Colonel Lane Fox (Pitt-Rivers), Mr John Evans and Mr John Stuart [presumably the Scottish genealogist, 1813–77]'. Evans and Pitt-Rivers, friends and colleagues of Lubbock, were well-known archaeologists.

As the Bill advanced with hopes of fruition, the Conservative Government suggested that instead of an 'ad hoc' body the Commission should consist of the Trustees of the British Museum, a neat solution, even if hardly suitable. In this form the Bill went forward and almost succeeded in 1880, passing the Commons but coming to grief in the Lords.[12] At the subsequent general election Gladstone came back to power but Lubbock lost his seat, returning shortly sitting for London University. Under the aegis of Gladstone a new Bill was introduced that became the 1882 Act. Now there was no Commission but merely an Inspector, no compulsion only permissive powers and the operating body the Office of Works, but in other respects following Lubbock's Bill. The responsible Minister was the First Commissioner, at that time a Cabinet post.

The changes were fundamental; the appointment of the first Inspector of Ancient Monuments, General Pitt-Rivers, deserves discussion. The Lubbock papers in the British Library throw light on this.[13]

The appointment was not left to the First Commissioner, Lefevre, but reserved to the First Lord of the Treasury, that is Gladstone, who seems to have left it to Lubbock to discuss with the First Commissioner.[13] From a shortlist Pitt-Rivers seemed the most suitable, and we have a copy of the letter from Lubbock virtually offering it to him[14]

> Lombard Street
> 25 Oct. 1882
> My dear Pitt-Rivers
> George Lefevre is going to talk to me about the Inspectorship of Ancient Monuments and I should much like to know your views on the Salary, Conditions, duties etc. which would be suitable. I suppose it must be a fixed salary and expenses

Who do you think would be the best man? You know the monuments as well as anyone but I presume you would not think of it?

Believe me

Yours most sincerely

John Lubbock

General Pitt-Rivers

It is the classic form which can be refused or accepted without loss of face. Pitt-Rivers was certainly thinking of it as this letter below shows.

Rushmore

Salisbury

Nov. 13 1882

My dear Lubbock

Lord Michael Grosvenor wrote to me about the Inspectorship of Ancient Monuments and I have said I would accept it. What is to be the exact designation by which the Inspector is to be known? The word Inspector is more frequently than not applied to a local Inspector.. Inspector General is a recognised title for such posts [...] I have been digging all through this beastly weather but without important result yet

Yours sincerely

A. Pitt-Rivers

Pitt-Rivers wished to include Ireland (which he knew) in his remit and have the title Inspector General. Was he thinking of Viollet-le-Duc in France, where that title was used? In fact the Treasury would agree to neither request but allowed the title of Inspector of Ancient Monuments in Great Britain, which he uses on the Cranborne Chase volumes.

In spite of these problems about titles he held the post for 17 years, seven of them salaried, carried out the famous excavations, built the Museum at Farnham, Dorset, to house them, as well as doing the visiting as Inspector, carrying that title to his death in 1900. He set up a staff of three or four young men to run his organisation.

(1)

(2)

(1) Wayland Smithy. Sketch by Tomkin in 1884. The figure acting as scale is that of Pitt Rivers (2) An unnamed stone circle in Scotland. The figure with notebook in hand, acting as scale, is Pitt Rivers

fig 14. General Pitt-Rivers at work as Inspector, used as a scale by Tomkin in drawings of 1884–5 (Thompson, 1960, fig. 10) (National Archive. Work 39/1-16)

Was all the effort in Parliament to achieve the 1882 Act worth it? The answer must surely be yes. As with some of Lubbock's other legislation it was the seedcorn from which large plants could grow. The Government had conceded a responsibility, and after the General's death it was extended to medieval monuments and Local Authorities were brought in, while in the main Act of 1913 compulsory powers were introduced. Still more important, it associated the Government Department with fieldwork and perhaps a more scientific outlook, even, dare one suggest, a less parochial, broader view of its duties.

Notes:

1. John Newman is the author of this volume: *East and North-East Kent*, p. 352
2. Lubbock, *1877a*, 37–50
3. Grant Duff (ed.), 1934, p. 21. Lubbock was Principal of the *Working Men's College of London*, 1883–98
4. The list is taken from Grant Duff (ed.), 1934, pp. 254, 255
5. *Prehistoric Times*, 1865, chapter 7
6. Information variously from diary and letters in British Library
7. *Reports from Committees*, viii, 1877, pp. 175–78
8. Lubbock, 1977b
9. *ibid.*, p. 264
10. *ibid.*, p. 262
11. Thompson, 2005
12. *Journal of the House of Lords* (1880), 43 Vic., p. 112
13. Add. MSS. 49645: pp. 112, 126, 128, 137, 163, 192, 203, 208.
14. Lubbock had no family connection with Pitt-Rivers at this date, for the courtship with Alice Fox-Pitt, the General's daughter, that led to Lubbock's second marriage is described in the diary in 1884.

7. The Essayist

Those who have the pleasure of attending the open meetings of schools and colleges and of giving away prizes are expected at the same time to offer such words of counsel and encouragement as the experience of the world might enable them to give those who are entering life.

Having been myself, when young, rather prone to suffer from low spirits I have at several of these gatherings taken the opportunity of dwelling on the privileges and blessings we enjoy and reprint here the substances of some of these addresses (omitting what was special to the circumstances of each case and freely making any alterations and additions which have since occurred to me).

Thus Lubbock introduced *The Pleasures of Life* in 1887. It was an instant success – so much so that after 20 editions a Part 2 with the same title was published in 1889 which even surpassed it, so that by 1914 over 200,000 copies of each had been printed (see Appendix 1). They were translated into perhaps a dozen European and Asian languages (the University Library has a Welsh translation!). By Victorian standards it was a major bestseller, which perhaps may indeed tell us as much, or even more, about the Victorian public as about the author. Before discussing how this fits into Lubbock's career, attention may be turned to one of his several interests in life, Education.

It might have been thought that with his own truncated education at Eton and its completion by intensive self-education, with a marked scientific orientation, he would have had little interest in the state of education in society. This was due in large measure to his desire to introduce science into the curriculum, where it had not previously been represented at all. He was not alone in this and others, notably Huxley, were moving in the same direction. It is not the intention here to enter into this subject, adequately covered by others, but nevertheless it was one of his most permanent achievements that cannot be ignored.

He served on three Royal Commissions dealing with educational matters. He inherited an association with the University of London, on the Senate of which he served, also as its Vice Chancellor, and from 1880 to 1900 he represented it in the House of Commons. As the letters in the British Library show, he had some misgivings about a man who had no form of university degree serving as its Vice Chancellor, but it did not deter him from accepting the offer to compete.

As his reputation grew, so he was involved in delivering the sort of lectures or speeches mentioned by himself at the beginning of this chapter. His time as Principal of the Working Men's College of London has been mentioned, and some of the lectures in *The Pleasures of Life* were delivered to that institution. Others were given to colleges in the north of England or Midlands, for after his boyhood he had little to do with the older educational establishments. An exception was his election to be Lord Rector of St Andrews, presumably by the student body referred to below.

Apart from the fact that his lectures were increasingly delivered to a non-professional and often young audience, two other factors favoured conversion from lecturer to a wider readership: the model of Bacon's essays and the 'optimism' of the period. In his choice of the hundred best books listed in his lecture to the Working Men's Club in lecture 5 of *Pleasures of Life*, five essayists are named, with Francis Bacon at the top. The table below (p.82) gives the most frequently quoted authors in the essays, with Bacon well represented, so he was very familiar with them. The 14-volume collected works of Bacon edited by Spedding and Ellis were published between 1857 and 1874, and at least four separate editions of Bacon's *Essays* were published in the 1870s; they were very popular with Victorians. Compare some of the titles: Bacon's 'Of Riches', 'Of Ambition', Of Adversity', with Lubbock's 'Wealth', 'Ambition', 'Adversity'.[1] Bacon's essays are as a rule shorter but they have, as do Lubbock's, the overloading with quotations discussed below. There is an analogy between them of the older experimental scientist giving his experience of life generally. I would suggest that it was an influence particularly at the beginning, but the financial success of the project carried more weight with the publisher if not the author.

'Scientific optimism' attributed by Sully[2] to Herbert Spencer, and of which he gave us a taste in the last chapter of *Prehistoric Times*, was very widespread and part indeed of the general ethos of Victorian optimism. The atmosphere of cynicism of today would have been quite out of place in England, at least at that time; in Germany it would have been a quite different story

It is worth turning attention to the slow development of the essays from the original lectures. In 1879 there was seen the first publication of two collections of lectures by Lubbock. *Scientific Lectures* was, as its name implies, a record of several lectures based on his professional interests, mainly but not only biological. *Addresses Political and Educational* deals with his other interests, for he had been in Parliament for nine years and was involved with his educational matters; he was already extending his interests well beyond biology. When in 1882 the British Association for the Advancement of Science, whose meetings he attended regularly, celebrated its fiftieth anniversary, he gave the Presidential address, which caused him to survey all areas of scientific advance over the period, *Fifty Years of Science*. This no doubt provided material that later be used for essays. His next work, *Chapters in Natural History* (1886), sounds like a popular work although I have not seen it.

This brings us to *The Pleasures of Life* (1887), its Preface being quoted at the beginning of this chapter. This explains how it was taken from lectures given to various colleges, which are named in a footnote at the beginning of each chapter except the last which is on 'Education'. This is probably the point at which he decided to think in terms of independent essays. The titles, such as 'The Blessing of Friends' and 'Pleasures of Travel', make one recoil. Chapter 3 is 'A Song of Books', leading us to chapter 4, 'The Choice of Books', where he gives his choice of 100 books – a formidable list that would tax a contemporary academic let alone the working men of the College in which he gave the lecture! We should probably regard it as a pious wish, a reflection of his own avid reading, for he was well known for carrying books in his greatcoat pocket as he commuted to the City. The other chapters are on familiar subjects, and because of their separate origin, without a theme apart from the overall one of pleasure of life (Appendix 6).

Part 1 of *Pleasures* had reached its twentieth edition in 1889, when Part 2 appeared. The public demand was insatiable and the two volumes had sold nearly half a million copies by 1914 (Appendix 1). The range of foreign translations is not recorded but probably reached double figures. The Preface of Part 2 says of Part 1:

> If, as I have been assured by many, my book has added to the powers of enjoying life and has proved a comfort in the hours of darkness that is the utmost I have ever hoped ... (preface)

Part 2 has 13 essays, unashamedly not based on lectures. There is much overlap in 'Ambition' and 'Health', but it strikes a more serious note, ending with 'Religion', 'Hope of Progress' and concluding with 'The Destiny of Man'. It must represent fairly general views: religion is a comfort and support, and doubt does not exclude faith; progress follows the two lines of science and education, slow but 'come it surely will'; on destiny he is speaking of afterlife – it can be peaceful – 'we may cherish a sure and certain hope that the interests and pleasures of this life are as nothing compared to those of the next'. On religion Lubbock had suspended judgement.

The Beauties of Nature (1892) are, as the title suggests, the beauties of the surrounding world: plants and animals and even the heavens and stars.

The Use of Life (1894) is in a serious vein, addressed to nature readers, with some quite memorable essays. The great question – how to live? 'Tact' – 'for success in life tact is more important than talent but not easily acquired by those to whom it does not come easily'; 'Money Matters'; 'Recreation'; 'Health' – alcohol and overeating the main problems; 'National Education' – 'knowledge is most precious for it can neither be stolen, given away, nor consumed'; Self-education'-on which of course Lubbock was an expert; 'Libraries'; 'Reading'; 'Patriotism' – the great Empire has sprung up gradually'; 'Citizenship' – 'The religion of Europe is not Christianity but the worship of the God of War'; 'Social Life'; 13, 'Industry', not only essential to success but has a healthy influence on moral character; 'Faith' – 'If we feel ourselves continually compelled to remain in ignorance and to suspend our judgement we need not on that account lose hope'. This represents Lubbock's views until the end of his life; 15 'Hope'; 16 'Charity'; 17, 'Character' – 'As a mere question of getting on in the world character and steadiness will do more for men than cleverness ... one great drawback of ambition is that it can never be satisfied'; 18, 'Religion' – 'Religion in daily life is a rule of conduct, a safeguard in prosperity, a comfort in adversity, a support in anxiety, a refuge in danger, consolation in sorrow, a haven of peace'.

Lubbock's next venture into this field covered the transition from the Victorian to the Edwardian period; *Essays and Addresses, 1900–1903*. Here he uses the word 'essays', applying it to the fifteen chapters. Both Huxley and Ruskin had recently died, and he gives absorbing accounts of both of them. He compared the effect of *Origin of Species* on Huxley and himself. Both had much in common in the three divisions of Huxley's work: Natural Science, Education and Metaphysics (fellow members of the Metaphysical Society and the X Club); 'For many years I was in close and intimate association with him.'

With Ruskin it was quite a different relationship, for although they were friends they differed on most points. He had a memorable visit to Avebury with Ruskin. He admired his drawings from nature. Lubbock also gives his views on Richard Jefferies and Macaulay. There are a further ten chapters on Manchester Public Library, the Order of Merit, the Early Closing Bill, Fiscal Policy, Municipal Trading, the Study of Nature, London County Council scholars (he was President of the Council) and the Churchmen's Union. The Church is the national recognition of the great mystery of existence.

There is a book listed, with the Micawberish title of *Happiness and Thrift* (1906) suggesting popular essays; a copy has never reached my hands.

Lubbock was 70 in 1904 but was still able to publish a *Rectorial Address delivered at St Andrews University* (1908). His election as Lord Rector by students is an indication of his popularity even with the youth in Scotland. His predecessors included Ruskin, John Stuart Mill, Froude, Balfour and, immediately before him, Carnegie. This lecture is of particular interest because it seems to have been published as delivered and not later garnished. It starts with 'Fellow Students'. 'A man who is entirely ignorant of the classics, even if he be a profound mathematician, biologist, chemist or geologist, is but a half-educated man.' We are on familiar ground: 'Many, if not most, of our troubles we made for ourselves.' ... 'Bodily pleasures are fleeting and often dearly bought.' The rest of the lecture need not be pursued.

The last work to be mentioned, *On Peace and Happiness* (1909), is again a collection of serious essays, although perhaps a little more repetitive than *Use of Life*. The three essays reproduced in Appendix 7 are taken from this volume. There are eighteen essays: 'On Happiness', 'The Body', 'The Mind', 'Aspiration' (Appendix 7a), 'Contentment', 'Adversity', 'Kindness', 'Education', 'On Friends and Enemies', 'On Riches', 'The Dread of Nature', 'The Love of Nature', 'Now' (Appendix 7b), 'Wisdom', 'Religion', 'Theology', 'Peace of Mind', 'The Peace of Nations' (Appendix 7c).

Clearly in *Peace and Happiness* there is much repetition, but in what Lubbock perhaps saw as his final endeavour on 'happiness' there is quite a lot of new development, particularly on Religion and Theology. Clearly we have come a long way from *Pleasures of Life*. The most dramatic change is in 'Peace of Nations' where he reveals his fear of an impending disastrous war. As early as 1894, above, he told us that there was no Christianity in Europe because everyone worshipped War. The Boer War had taken place in the intervening period. Every year Lubbock went to Switzerland or Germany and he was President of the Anglo-German Society, so he was very well-informed on what was going on both at home and abroad in the field of armaments or, more important, on the mood and display of military and naval hardware. The article, for it is more that than an essay, gives ample statistics of the weapons. The terrible aspect of his premonition is that war was not only prepared for but actually wanted by many. He did not live to see his fearful premonition realised for he died in 1913. He was a patriot but no lover of war. This aspect of Lubbock is often overlooked.

Quotations in Lubbock's Essays

Key to table on page 83:
A. *Pleasures of Life* – 1, Duty of Happiness (1887)
B. *Pleasures of Life* – *Part 2*, Ambition (1889)
C. *Pleasures of Life* – *Part 2*, The Destiny of Man (1889)
D. *Peace and Happiness*, Aspiration (1909)
E. *Peace and Happiness*, Now (1909)
F. *Peace and Happiness*, On Happiness (1909)
G. *Peace and Happiness*, The Body (1909)
H. *Peace and Happiness*, The Mind (1909)
I. *Peace and Happiness*, Contentment (1909)

Before leaving the essays one matter needs mention:

> Again, some have complained that there is too much quotation too little of my own. This I take to be in reality a great compliment; I have not striven to be original ...
> (p. 81)

Lubbock met his critics in the Preface of *Pleasures of Life, Part 2.*

However, the criticism is very fair, for the volume of quotation can be sometimes a little overwhelming.

The table on page 83 shows figures of samples from nine essays, A–C from *The Pleasures of Life* and the last six from *Peace and Happiness* 20 years later. Where there is a repetition of the same author in the same essay it is included in the table, but the majority of quotations are once from each author, so that the omitted quotations from different authors not listed but included in the total are single ones. For example, in the column from the 'The Duty of Happiness' in *Pleasures of Life, Part 1*, only five authors have multiple quotations, so Lubbock took some care in the 47 quotations not to use an author more than once. It can hardly be accidental, and probably required a catalogue or index. Whether he was trying to demonstrate his acquaintance with the 100 authors in his chosen list or simply did not want an author too much quoted, it is of course impossible to say.

There are no surprises in the choice of authors – all are eminently quotable. He normally quotes French authors in French, sometimes with translation, but German authors like Goethe are normally in translation. Latin authors are quoted in Latin, but Greek usually in translation. The educated public for which Lubbock wrote had a much greater knowledge and reverence for Classical writers than would be the case today.

Apart from fluency in French and probably in German, the chapter on language in *Origin of Civilisation* shows he had considerable linguistic interests, as a pupil of Max Müller, so that quotation from the *Mahabarata* is not a surprise. Although the essays are in no sense religious sermons, the quotations from the Old (especially) and New Testaments would be reassuring to the reader. What is markedly absent is quotation from novelists like Dickens, Thackeray or the Brontës: contemporary poetry, yes, but prose fiction, no.

If I may quote again from the Preface of *Pleasures of Life, Part 2*:

> If, as I have been assured by many that my book has added to their powers of enjoying life, and has proved a comfort in the hours of darkness, that is indeed a complete reward and is the utmost I have ever hoped ... (preface)

In Victorian times there were no Government counsellors, no psychiatrists to advise, and Church of England priests were never cast in that role. Self-counselling through books was the alternative available; Lubbock's *Pleasures of Life* were designed to meet this need, the wisdom of a well-known and successful man and scientist that could be consulted, if necessary in secret. The demand for this helps to explain the huge sales. The later essays were less counselling in style and had of course fewer sales, although they normally sold well.

The two aspects of the essays that are worth bearing in mind are the light they throw on Lubbock himself, his religious views or lack of them, the advantages of belief, although not to be discouraged if faith failed. Often they show to what he attributed his own success. They also shed some light on some aspects of Victorian society, particularly the sort of heart-searching that went on about religious belief, on progress and the polarised divisions between rich and poor, of which Lubbock was acutely aware. On the other hand, the complete self-assurance, the patriotism and belief in their own values are evident. In some respects the contrast with modern society is profound, in others little altered.

Notes:
1. Everyman's edition of Bacon's *Essays* (1625) has been used.
2. Sully, 1884

	A	B	C	D	E	F	G	H	I
Old Testament			1		6	1	1	1	
New Testament			1		1	1	2	1	
Homer	1							1	
Plato			3						
Pindar					1				2
Plutarch		1				1		2	1
Cicero		1	4	2		1	1		1
Horace					1				
Seneca	3		1	1	1	2		1	
Aurelius, Marcus	2	1							
Epictetus	4		1						1
Epicurus	1					1			
St. Augustine				1		1			
Bede			1				1		
Thomas a Kempis					1	2			
Shakespeare	1		3	6	4	3	4	3	5
Bacon	3	3		4	2	1	1		
Browne, Sir Thomas								2	
Selden						1			
La Rochefoucauld							1		
Spinoza							1		
Milton				1				3	
La Bruyere	1			1					
Dryden								2	
Chesterfield					1				
Rousseau	2			2					
Shelley			3						
Macaulay				2				1	
Scott, Walter				1				1	
Goethe		1				2			1
Joubert					1				2
Shelley									
Taylor, Jeremy	1				1		1		
Kingsley						1			
Ruskin	1			1	1				
Carroll, Lewis	1								
Tennyson		1							1
Schopenhauer					1				
Longfellow			1					1	
Amiel						2			
Huxley				1		1		1	
Mahabarata								1	
TOTALS with other quoted writers included	47	17	26	29	32	38	18	34	33

8. Lubbock in a Broader Context

There can be no doubt about Lubbock's esteem, respect and even fame amongst the public in general. At his death his widow received condolences from the King and Queen, presumably on behalf of the Nation. This was a stamp of approval enough from the Establishment, but his election as Rector of St Andrews by students shows approval by youth, usually reluctant to give it. No doubt they were middle-class students wanting advice on conduct in their coming careers. The host of appointments to societies and institutions built up into the shape of a carinated bowl, or perhaps the cup that was overflowing, usually as president or chairman, is surely an impressive token of his high regard in the world of learning and scholarship, and in this bowl section not only English but foreign bodies are represented (fig. 15). This book has described in part how the appointments were rewards for a remarkably successful career, but why did his reputation suffer so badly after his death in 1913?

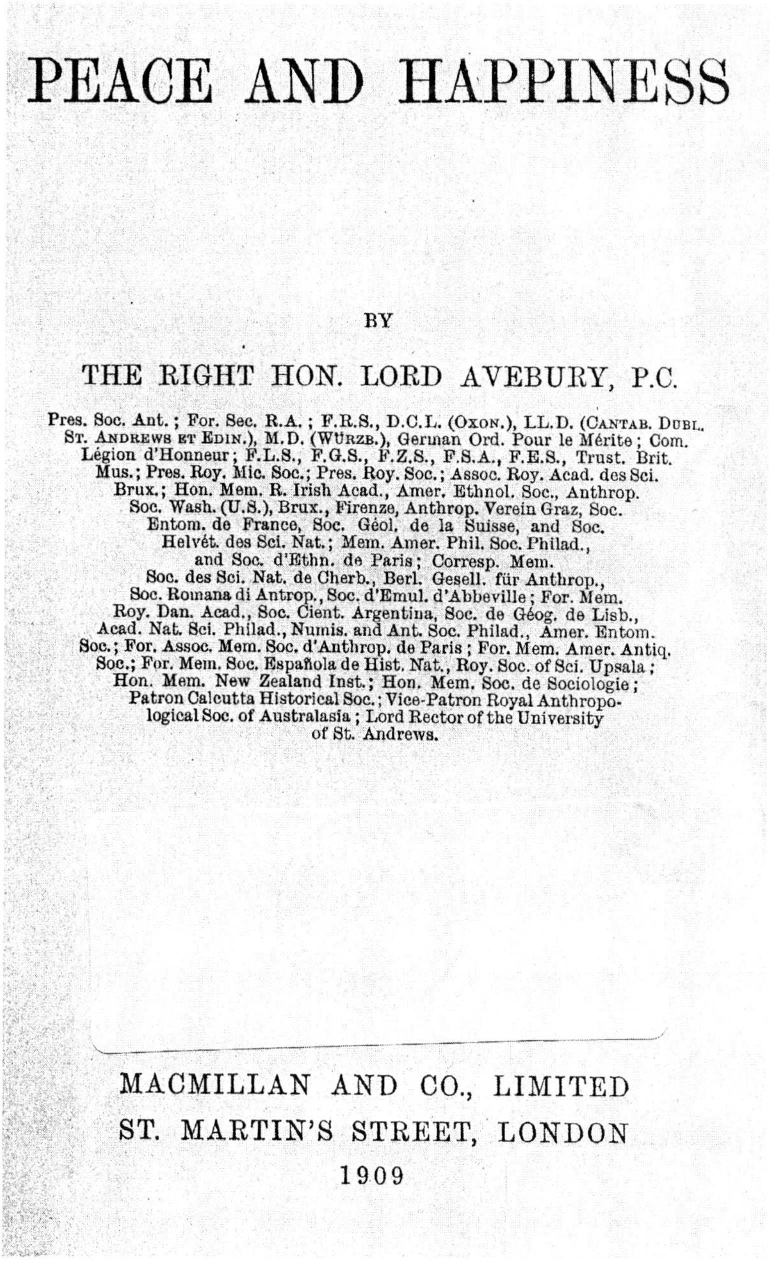

PEACE AND HAPPINESS

BY

THE RIGHT HON. LORD AVEBURY, P.C.

Pres. Soc. Ant. ; For. Sec. R.A. ; F.R.S., D.C.L. (OXON.), LL.D. (CANTAB. DUBL.
ST. ANDREWS ET EDIN.), M.D. (WÜRZB.), German Ord. Pour le Mérite ; Com.
Légion d'Honneur ; F.L.S., F.G.S., F.Z.S., F.S.A., F.E.S., Trust. Brit.
Mus.; Pres. Roy. Mic. Soc.; Pres. Roy. Soc.; Assoc. Roy. Acad. des Sci.
Brux.; Hon. Mem. R. Irish Acad., Amer. Ethnol. Soc., Anthrop.
Soc. Wash. (U.S.), Brux., Firenze, Anthrop. Verein Graz, Soc.
Entom. de France, Soc. Géol. de la Suisse, and Soc.
Helvét. des Sci. Nat.; Mem. Amer. Phil. Soc. Philad.,
and Soc. d'Ethn. de Paris ; Corresp. Mem.
Soc. des Sci. Nat. de Cherb., Berl. Gesell. für Anthrop.,
Soc. Romana di Antrop., Soc. d'Emul. d'Abbeville ; For. Mem.
Roy. Dan. Acad., Soc. Cient. Argentina, Soc. de Géog. de Lisb.,
Acad. Nat. Sci. Philad., Numis. and Ant. Soc. Philad., Amer. Entom.
Soc.; For. Assoc. Mem. Soc. d'Anthrop. de Paris ; For. Mem. Amer. Antiq.
Soc.; For. Mem. Soc. Española de Hist. Nat., Roy. Soc. of Sci. Upsala ;
Hon. Mem. New Zealand Inst.; Hon. Mem. Soc. de Sociologie ;
Patron Calcutta Historical Soc.; Vice-Patron Royal Anthropo-
logical Soc. of Australasia ; Lord Rector of the University
of St. Andrews.

MACMILLAN AND CO., LIMITED

ST. MARTIN'S STREET, LONDON

1909

fig 15. Title page of *Peace and Happiness* showing Lubbock's titles at age 75, arranged to give outline of carinated bowl (Lubbock, 1909)

There are many reasons. The Great War starting eighteen months after his death was a powerful shock to the whole social fabric, and the fact that Lubbock had foreseen it and warned against it only rubbed salt into the wound. The 1920s were a different world from the Edwardian era, let alone the Victorian one to which Lubbock belonged. Apart from technological transformation – wireless, cinema, refrigerators, cheap motor cars – the political world completely altered, and the changes accelerated into the 1930s. By then the hostility and contempt for all things Victorian – the very word denoting pejorative over-tones – was such that a banker with money who had been successful in several fields could hardly escape obloquy. So those who admire, or at all events respect, people of the period have an uphill task in making themselves heard. Let us turn to review some of the subjects discussed in the previous chapters.

Lubbock was probably just long enough at Eton College to imbibe some of its characteristics, and it is likely that the foundation of his not insignificant Classical knowledge was laid there; we know from his curriculum of self-education that he built on that. His father by his daily mathematical lessons made his contribution. He had embarked on the daily, or perhaps twice or more weekly, commuter trip (made possible by the new railways) described by Herbert Spencer. It must have been lonely after Eton, a child or boy in his teens among adults in a bustling city who by his position could hardly associate with other boys. London can be very lonely, and he himself regarded it as the unhappiest period of his life. Only from about 1852 could he meet the adult world on its own terms. By this time he had already established a fairly close friendship with Darwin. His first marriage in 1856 led to his having to leave High Elms, and the Preface to *Prehistoric Times* (1865) is signed Chisslehurst.

His friendship with Darwin was without doubt the most formative element in his life; his long periods of 'work with microscope' in his self-education, we may recall, was done with a microscope that Darwin had acquired for his father to give the boy. He was perhaps 15 then but at 19 in 1853 his first scientific paper appeared, and by then he and Darwin were on friendship terms at an adult level. The picture that one letter gives (page 6) of Mrs Darwin reading

Prehistoric Times aloud (but only the chapters on 'savages' at the end) is a charming one. It was a close friendship in which Lubbock assisted Darwin in cataloguing his collections. In later life he had a reverence for Darwin; in the diary in 1882, when Darwin died, Lubbock spoke of his advice being 'like a breath of sea air'. The letters in the British Library reveal that a petition drawn up by some Members of Parliament was conveyed by Lubbock to the Dean of Westminster asking for Darwin's burial in the Abbey. His relatives would have preferred a burial at Downe. With an aristocratic group, Lubbock and Huxley were pall bearers.

What part did Lubbock play in the spread of Darwin's evolutionary ideas to a wider audience? In science probably a minor one compared to Huxley or indeed Darwin himself; in archaeology a much greater part. If Prestwich and Lyell established the antiquity of man, Lubbock saw it as the birth of a new subject set between geology and history. The seven editions of *Prehistoric Times*, 1865–1913, with their chronological inversion of chapters like a geological section, emphasised this. In archaeology there are the classifiers in museum style like Sir John Evans, with his splendid works on stone and bronze tools, or the diggers like Bateman and Greenwell or at a more scientific level Pitt Rivers, or last the thinkers like Lubbock. The intellectual basis of *Prehistoric Times* was given in its last chapter (Appendix 5), crude to modern eyes but eminently worth reading. No wonder Darwin said that no one who had written that chapter could possibly waste his time in politics, for Lubbock made his first attempt in 1865 to enter the House of Commons.

One of the innovative features of the book was the description of modern primitives; for the modern student of the middle or lower Palaeolithic it is difficult to appreciate the problems and solutions needed for survival when equipped with a very sparse technology. Modern primitives often give us an insight into this, particularly if the climatic conditions and animal and plant life were similar in both cases. This is not to say that by projecting the known on to the unknown the people were culturally similar, and certainly not identical. In those remote periods the people were even physically different from modern primitives.

If we can describe Lubbock as the founder of prehistoric archaeology as a subject to study, he was a close second in the foundation of anthropology as an independent subject, the palm going rather to E. B. Tylor. The title of Lubbock's *Origin of Civilisation* (1870) seems to be derived from Tylor's subtitle to *Researches into the Early History of Man and the Development of Civilisation*. Anthropologists then saw themselves as tracing the ascent from 'savagery to civilisation'. The extent to which both evolution and the work of Lubbock and Tylor reached is illustrated by Walter Bagehot; his famous work, *The English Constitution* (1865), was followed by *Physics and Politics* (1872), where he had *thoughts on the Application of the Principles of 'Natural Selection' and 'Inheritance' to Political Society'*. In a chapter on nation-making (p. 112) we are told:

> Investigations whose acuteness and diligence can hardly be surpassed – Sir John Lubbock and Mr Tylor are the chiefs among them – have collected so much and explained so much that they have left a fairly vivid result. (p. 112)

Lubbock did not just follow Tylor but pursued lines of his own, although he did not grasp the meaning of culture in the way Tylor had learnt it in Germany.

In many ways, in his anthropological guise Lubbock touched on the very heart of Victorian society: marriage, male or female dominance, the moral character of society, religion and so on. He often found certain aspects of savage life too shocking to describe, which no doubt thrilled many readers, for his book ran to six editions. Mute flints are not so interesting to biologists as living beings who just left their litter behind, and we may recall Darwin reading the last chapters on savages first in Lubbock's book! Although Lubbock's contribution was greatest in prehistoric archaeology, he was perhaps better known for his second book, as is suggested by the references to his lectures on savages in the diary, sometimes at Downe.

Lubbock's optimism was shared by many in Victorian society, particularly among naturalists, with Herbert Spencer as its chief exponent.[1] It is difficult for us today to appreciate the shock produced by the revelations about the world around us and the readily available information[2] about its wonders. It created an almost childlike excitement which we who are used to microscopes and astronomical telescopes take for granted: Lubbock had his own archaeological reasons for optimism.

First it was necessary to prove 'progress', on which the whole argument hung. There was indeed technological improvement which Lubbock believed happened not by diffusion but independently after the spread of recognisable human beings from one original centre. There was other evidence of progress but the only real numerical and concrete one was increase in population. So he used the more or less reliable data from different areas of America to show how the density of population, so many or so few per square mile, varied according to the way of life of Indians living there, with a very low level only supporting a small population. Note how comparison with modern primitives is basic to the whole argument. One projected this data on to the way of life assumed from the archaeological evidence for the prehistoric and later populations, which suggested very substantial increase of density in the Swiss lake villages over the Danish kitchen middens. Gordon Childe used the same line of argument to justify his 'Neolithic Revolution'. If increase in density of population was progress, then Lubbock's generation was at its front edge, so the future was very rosy as 'progress' pursued its relentless course forward. Lubbock thought man had discarded 'Natural Selection' which still operated in the rest of the natural world; it was a very comforting belief and certainly led to optimism.

Unfortunately there was a dark cloud overhanging this – *Sin*. This was evidently the original sin of Lubbock's devout boyhood revealed in his self-education programme. This deep belief was modified into one of 'suspended judgment' on the question of God's existence. In his essays he tells us that loss of faith did not mean loss of hope. This sort of attitude was probably widespread among Victorians and seems to have been the attitude of my grandfather (born 1867), although I never discussed it with him.

In science his contribution was surely not insignificant: books like Seedlings and Springtails, or his work on animal behaviour, senses of animals and so on. *Ants, Bees and Wasps* brought him fame certainly, and surely brought knowledge to the public about very familiar creatures, quite apart from the research and the highly original way of carrying it out. Obviously, advances since then have left it far behind. A main contribution to science was his steady support for introducing it into the school curriculum, for before it had been an unknown subject for children, as in his time at Eton. It is a sobering thought that if his father had not insisted on him leaving Eton to help in their City bank he might never have studied science with Darwin. In the essays, education and science were regarded as linchpins of future progress.

Of the 30-odd Acts that he started as Bills, perhaps the Bank Holiday Act had most impact on the country at large, and still remains on the statute books with such alterations made, as required, as it allowed. The addition of secular holidays to the existing religious ones was a significant one. Again the Ancient Monuments Act of 1882, even much altered by the Government, was 'consolidated' into the 1913 Act and started a long sequence of legislation in this field. Surely no single person has introduced so many Bills that covered Great Britain and, in the case of the 1882 Act, even Ireland.

Of all parts of Lubbock's writing, the essays were the most popular, issued in many different cheap editions, particularly of course the two parts of *The Pleasures of Life* with their huge sales. This kind of wisdom on conduct and careers, supported by quotations from many Classical authors, had a special appeal to Victorians, full of adages and aphorisms. Faced with heady patriotism, not to say jingoism, the essays quickly became obsolete, especially as Lubbock made no secret of his disapproval of war and massive armaments (Appendix 7c).

The wide range of Lubbock's activities are made even more remarkable by his consistent success in most of them. Today they would be quite beyond any single person to attempt, let alone successfully complete. Not all have been described in this book: his success in banking, association with a company promoting electric lighting with Edison's bulbs, and so on. Polymaths are often accused of not taking anything far enough, but most of us would be happy to have reached as far as Lubbock in any of the pursuits he followed.

Notes:

1. Sully, 1884
2. Lightman, 2007; O'Connor, 2008

Appendix 1

Books written by Lubbock, with scale of issue or print run by 1914

There is a list of Lubbock's books in Hutchinson, 1914, vol. 2, p.321, and at the end of the same volume Macmillans give a list with print runs, for they were Lubbock's main publisher. Books were published in batches of 1,000, and so for example '33rd thousand' would indicate that 33,000 volumes were printed and bound. The almost complete series in the Cambridge University Library has been used to supplement the lists mentioned, but because of changed titles this list is not quite complete. Lubbock's extensive periodical publication is not included but a probably fairly full number are listed in the articles in his daughter's publication (Grant Duff, 1934). No details of print runs are available from books published by other publishers used by Lubbock apart from Macmillans.

1865	*Prehistoric Times as Illustrated by Ancient Remains and the Manners and Customs of Modern Savages*	Williams and Norgate 7 editions to 1913
1870	*The Origin of Civilisation and the Primitive Condition of Man*	Longmans 6 editions to 1902
1871	*Monograph of the Collembola and Thysanura*	Ray Society
1873	*The Origin and Metamorphosis of Insects*	Macmillan
1873	*On the Bank Act of 1844*	
1874	*British Wild Flowers Considered in Relation to Insects*	Macmillan 11th thousand
1878	*On Certain Relations Between Plants and Insects*	
1879	*Addresses, Political and Educational*	Macmillan
1879	*Scientific Lectures*	Macmillan 4th thousand
1881	*Fifty Years of Science*	Macmillan 6th edition
1882	*Ants, Bees and Wasps*	Kegan Paul Int Sc. S. 17th edition
1884	*Proportional Representation*	
1885	*On Representation*	Swan Sonnenschein
1886	*Flowers, Fruit and Leaves*	Macmillan. Nat. Ser.
1886	*Chapters in Popular Natural History*	N. H. Soc
1887	*Nationalities of United Kingdom*	
1887	*The Pleasures of Life, Part 1*	Macmillan 272nd thousand
1888	*On the Senses, Instincts and Intelligence of Animals*	Kegan Paul 5th edition. Int. Sc. S

1889	*The Pleasures of Life, Part 2*	Macmillan
		232nd thousand
1889	*La Vie des Plantes*	J. B. Bailliere et Fils
1892	*The Beauties of Nature*	Macmillan
		87th thousand
1892	*On Seedlings*, 2 vols.	Kegan Paul
1894	*The Use of Life*	Macmillan
		186th thousand
1896	*The Scenery of Switzerland*	5th edition
1899	*On Buds and Stipules*	Kegan Paul Int. Sc. S.
1901	*The King's Weigh House*	
1901	*The Scenery of England*	Macmillan
		5th edition
1902	*Coins and Currency*	John Murray
1903	*Essays and Addresses, 1900–1903*	Macmillan
1904	*Free Trade*	Macmillan
		4th edition
1905	*Notes on the Life History of British Flowering Plants*	Macmillan
1906	*Happiness and Thrift*	Macmillan
1906	*On Municipal and National Trading*	Macmillan
		3rd Impression
1908	*Address at St Andrews University*	
1909	*On Peace and Happiness*	Macmillan
		3rd Impression
1911	*Marriage, Totemism and Religion*	Macmillan

Appendix 2

Dramatis Personae

Bagehot, Walter (1825–1877) Economist and Journalist. Gold medallist in intellectual and moral philosophy in London. Apart from *The English Constitution* he wrote *Physics and Politics or Thoughts on the Application of the Principles of 'Natural Selection' and 'Inheritance' to Political Society* which made use of Lubbock's and Tylor's work.

Busk, George (1807–1886) Surgeon who did important work with the microscope. Founder member of Microscopical Society. Moved from Greenwich to Harley Street but gave up practice for study of palaeontology (Neanderthal skull) and ethnology. Travelled in Europe with Lubbock in the 1860's. X Club.

Chambers, Robert (1802–1871) Publisher in Edinburgh. From geological record assumed fossils showed evolution in *Vestiges of Creation* published anonymously in 1844 with subsequent editions. Prepared public to some extent for evolution in *Origin of Species* in 1859.

Christy, Henry (1810–1865) Banker and ethnologist. Travelled in East, Scandinavia and North America where he met Tylor. Financed Lartet's excavations in Dordogne in early 1860s.

Evans, Sir John (1823–1908) Paper manufacturer, archaeologist and numismatist. Author of *The Ancient Stone Implements of Great Britain* (1872) and *The Ancient Bronze Implements of Great Britain* (1881).

Fergusson, James (1808–1886) Writer on architecture. Published *History of Architecture in all Countries* in 1865–7, and *Fire and Serpent Worship* in 1868

Franks, Sir Augustus (1826–1897) Trinity College, Cambridge. Working life at British Museum as Keeper of Medieval Antiquities. Proposed Commissioner in Lubbock's Bill.

Galton, Sir Francis (1822–1911) Cousin of Darwin. Genealogist or eugenics specialist influenced by Darwin's *Origin of Species*. Darwin stayed with him.

Greg, Robert Hyde (1795–1875) Economist and antiquary. Contributed to Manchester Literary Society including work on site of Troy. Probably the 'poor Greg' (he was then 77) who accompanied Lubbock's party that went down the Danube in 1872 to Schliemann's excavations at Troy.

Grant Duff, Sir Mountstuart E. (1829–1906) Liberal MP 1857–1881, close friend and travel companion of Lubbock from 1870s, interrupted by a short period in India. Published diary 1851–1905 in fourteen volumes. FRS.

Hooker, Sir Joseph (1817–1911) Botanist and traveller. Close friend of Darwin and worked on *Origin of Species* with him. Assistant at Kew Gardens from 1855 and Director from 1865, retired from it 1885. Many publications on flora from different parts of world. X Club.

Huxley, Thomas (1825–1895) Man of science. Medical background. Professor at Royal College of Surgeons. Many publications. Close friend of Darwin, vigorous supporter of evolution and natural selection. President of Royal Society. Member of X Club.

Kingsley, Charles (1813–1875) Author. Educated at Cambridge and priest at Eversley. Traveller. Novelist – *Water Babies*. Professor of Modern History at Cambridge. Interested in natural history. Attempted to reconcile science and religion. Controversy with Newman.

Lyell, Sir Charles (1797–1875) Geologist, author of *Principles of Geology*, 3 vols 1830–33. *Antiquity of Man*, 1873; close friend and adviser to Darwin but much older and more of a guide and adviser.

MacLennan, John Ferguson (1827–1891) Anthropologist. Author of *Primitive Marriage*, inventing words endogamy and exogamy, and describer of marriage by capture. Correspondence with Lubbock in British Library.

Maine, Sir Henry (1822–1888) Teacher and writer on law and author of *Ancient Law; its early History and its relation to Modern Ideas*, 1861. Held academic posts at Cambridge and Oxford. Wrote also *Village Communities*, 1877.

Owen, Sir Richard (1804–1892) Distinguished naturalist who worked at the British Museum and then South Kensington (Natural History) Museum. He was especially concerned with classification of fossil fauna and published extensively. Very critical of the *Origin of Species* and firm opponent of Darwin and Lubbock but somewhat isolated from mainstream scientific opinion by his rather fierce style.

Pitt-Rivers, Augustus Henry (Lane Fox) (1827–1900) He took the name Pitt-Rivers under the terms of inheritance of the Cranborne Chase estate, 1880. From the time of The Great Exhibition he collected tools and weapons to illustrate their typological development, but is more famous for his excavations in Cranborne Chase, Dorset, after his appointment as Inspector of Ancient Monuments, 1883, published in four great volumes.

Prestwich, Sir Joseph (1812–1896) Geologist. London and Oxford. Authenticated human tools with extinct fauna to Roll Society 1859.

Spencer, Herbert (1820–1903) Philosopher. Started his career as engineer on the railway lines then being built and then turned to philosophy. Best known for *Social Statics*, 1851 and then the various volumes of his *System of Synthetic Philosophy*, published over several years. X Club.

Tylor, Sir Edward Burnett (1832–1917) Anthropologist. First Professor of Anthropology at Oxford. Knew Lubbock whom he clearly influenced by his two books, *Researches in the Early History of Mankind and the Development of Civilisation*, 1865, and *Primitive Culture*, 1871. Travelled in Germany, from where he derived his concept of culture, and in Mexico where he met Christy.

Tyndall, John (1820–1893) Born in Dublin. Natural Philosopher. Engineer in early life. Friend of Huxley. Germany. Became Professor of Natural Philosophy at Royal Institution. Physicist. X Club.

Wallace, Alfred Russell (1823–1913) Naturalist. Trip to Amazon in 1848 and Moluccas in 1858 when he came to conclusion on Natural Selection and sent paper to Darwin leading to papers in Linnaean Society. Malay Archipelago 1858–62. FRS 1893. Important book *On the Geographical Distribution of Animals*.

Wilson, Sir Daniel (1816–1892) Archaeologist and educational reformer. Hon. Secretary of Scottish Antiquaries and Professor of History and English Literature at Toronto. 1853, *Archaeology and Prehistoric Annals of Scotland*.

Wright, Thomas (1810–1877) Antiquary. Trinity College Cambridge. Literary, with main interest in Saxon and Medieval period, received State Pension of £100. Thought Bronze Age bronzes were Roman which led to dispute with Lubbock. Strong religious views and opposed to evolution.

Appendix 3

Legislation Introduced by Sir John Lubbock, Lord Avebury
This list is taken from Grant Duff (ed.), 1934, pp. 254–5.

1871	Bank Holidays Act
1873	Tithe Commutations Act Amendment Act
1874	Apothecaries Act
1874	Falsification of Accounts Act
1875	College of Surgeons Act
1876	University of London Medical Amendment Act
1877	Absconding Debtors Act
1878	Dental Practitioners Act
1879	Bankers Books Evidence Act
1880	Wild Birds Protection Act
1882	Ancient Monuments Act
1882	Bills of Exchange Act
1883	Companies Colonial Registers Act
1884	Greek Marriages Act
1886	Shop Hours Regulation Act
1889	Factory Act Amendment Act

1890	Open Spaces Act
1890	Metropolis Management, Buildings Act Amendment Act
1892	Public Libraries Act
1898	Companies Acts Amendment Act
1900	Seats for Shop Assistants Act Amendment Act
1901	Ancient Monuments Act Amendment Act
1903	County Courts Jurisdiction Extension Act
1904	Shop Hours Act (Early Closing)
1905	Closing of Licensed Premises (Christmas) Act
1906	Limited Partnership Act
1907	Companies (Debentures) Act
1908	Municipal Franchise Companies Bill
1908	Sunday Closing (Shops) Bill
1908	Importation of Plumage Prohibition Bill

Appendix 4

The Schedule to the Ancient Monuments Act, 1882
The purpose of reciting this Schedule is to demonstrate that prehistoric monuments were the principal monuments to be preserved under the terms of the Act; those in England and Wales exclusively so, but with an admixture of early Christian in Scotland and Ireland. The list is as published, with its own spelling, with Ireland being omitted.

THE SCHEDULE

List of Monuments to which Act Applies
England and Wales

	County	Parish
The tumulus and dolmen, Plas Newydd Anglesea	Anglesea	Llandedwen
The tumulus known as Wayland Smith's Forge	Berkshire	Ashbury
Uffington Castle	"	Uffington
The stone circle known as Long Meg and her Daughters, near Penrith	Cumberland	Addingham
The stone circle on Castle Rigg, near Keswick	"	Crossthwaite
The stone circles on Burn Moor	"	St Bees
The stone circle known as the Nine Ladies, Stanton Moor	Derbyshire	Bakewell
The tumulus known as Arbor Low	"	"
Hob Hurst's House and Hut, Bastow Moor	"	"
Minning Low	"	Brassington
Arthur's Quoit, Gower	Glamorganshire	Llanrhidian
The tumulus at Uley	Gloucestershire	Uley
Kits Coty House	Kent	Aylesford
Danes Camp	Northamptonshire	Hardingstone
Castle Dykes	"	Farthingstone
The Rollrich Stones	Oxfordshire	Little Rollright
The Pentre Evan Cromlech	Pembrokeshire	Nevern
The ancient stones at Stanton Drew	Somersetshire	Stanton Drew

The chambered tumulus at Stoney Littleton, Wellow	"	Wellow
Cadbury Castle	"	South Cadbury
Mayborough, near Penrith	Westmorland	Barton
Arthur's Round Table	"	"
The group of stones known as Stonehenge	Wiltshire	Amesbury
Old Sarum	"	–
The Vallum at Abury, the Sarsen stones with the same, those along the	"	Abury
Kennet Avenue, and the group between		
Abury and Beckhampton		
The long barrow at West Kennet, near Marlborough	"	West Kennet
Silbury Hill	"	Abury
The Dolmen (Devil's Den), near Marlborough	"	Fyfield
Barbury Castle	"	Ogbourne, St Andrews, and Swindon

Scotland

The Bass of Inverury	Aberdeenshire	Inverurie
The vitrified fort on the hill of Noath	"	Rhynie
The pillar and stone at Newton-in-the-Garioch	"	Culsalmond
The circular walled structure called "Edin's Hall" on Cockburn Law	Berwickshire	Dunse
The British walled settlement enclosing huts at Harefaulds in Lauderdale	"	Lauder
The Dun of Dornadilla	Sutherlandshire	Durness

The sculptured stone called Suenos Stone, near Forres		
The cross slab with inscription in the churchyard of St Vigeans	Forfarshire	St Vigeans
The British forts, on the hills, called "The Black and White Cathertuns"	"	Meumir
A group of remains and pillars on a haugh at Clava on the banks of the Nairn	Inverness	Croy and Daleross
The Pictish towers on Glenelg	"	Glenelg
The Cairns, with chambers and galleries partially dilapidated	Kirkcudbrightshire	Minnigaff
The Catstane, an inscribed pillar	Linlithgow	Kirkliston
The Ring of Brogar and other stone pillars at Stennis in Orkney and the neighbouring pillars	Orkney	Firth and Stennis
The chambered mound of Maeshowe	"	"
The stones of Callernish	Ross	Uig
The Burgh of Clickanim	Shetland	Sound
The Pictish tower at Mousa in Shetland	"	Dunrossness
The inscribed slab standing on the roadside leading from Wigton to Whithorn and about a mile from Whithorn	Wigtonshire	Whithorn
Two stones, with incised crosses, on a mound in a field at Langgangairn	"	New Luce
The pillars at Kirkmadrine	"	Stoneykirk

Ireland
(omitted here)

Appendix 5

The Last Chapter of *Prehistoric Times*
This is chapter 14 of the first edition of *Prehistoric Times*, 1865, but after the insertion of two new chapters in the thoroughly revised book it became chapter 16 for the second (1869) and later editions. The first edition was the one Darwin saw, which is used here. It has been substantially shortened and footnotes omitted.

14. Concluding Remarks
I have already expressed my belief that the simpler arts and implements have been independently invented by various tribes, and in very different parts of the world. Even at the present day we may, I think, obtain glimpses of the manner in which they were or may have been invented. Some monkeys are said to use clubs, and to throw sticks and stones at those who intrude upon them. We know that they use round stones for cracking nuts, and surely a very small step would lead from that to the application of a sharp stone for cutting. When the edge becomes blunt, it would be thrown away and another chosen but after a while, accident, if not reflection, would show, that a round

stone would crack other stones as well as nuts and thus the savage would make sharp-edged stones for himself. At first as we see in the drift specimens, these would be coarse and rough, but gradually the pieces chipped off would become smaller. ... From pressure to polishing would again be but a small step ...

The chimpanzee builds himself a house or shelter almost equal to that of some savages. Our earliest ancestors therefore may have had this art ... they could not fail to observe, and perhaps to copy, the houses which various species of animals construct for themselves.

The Esquimaux have no pottery: they use hollow stones as a substitute, but we have seen how they sometimes improve upon these by a rim of clay. To extend this rim, diminish and at last replace the stone is an obvious process. Other similar cases might be mentioned in which by a very simple and apparently obvious process improvement is secured. It seems very improbable any such advantage should ever be lost again. There is no evidence, says Mr Tylor; 'of any tribe giving up the use of the spindle to twist their thread by hand, or having been in the habit of working the fire-drill with a thong, and going back to the clumsier practice of working it without, and it is even hard to fancy such a thing happening'. What follows from this argument? Evidently that the lowest races of existing savages must, always assuming the common origin of the human race, be at least as far advanced as were our ancestors when they spread over the earth's surface.

What then must have been their condition? They were ignorant of pottery, for the Esquimaux, the Polynesians, the Australians, some North and South American tribes, and many other savage races, have none even now, or at least had none until quite lately. They had no bows and arrows, for these weapons were unknown to the Australians and New Zealanders; their boats for the same reason must have been of the rudest possible character; they were naked, and ignorant of the art of spinning; they had no knowledge of agriculture and probably no domestic animal but the dog ...

The same argument may be applied to the mental condition of savages. That our earliest ancestors could have counted to ten is very improbable, considering that so many races now in existence cannot get beyond four. On the other hand it is very improbable that man can have existed in a lower condition than that thus indicated. So long indeed as he was confined to the tropics he may have found a succession of fruits, and have lived as monkeys do now. Indeed according to Bates, this is the case with some of the Brazilian Indians. 'The monkeys' he says' 'lead in fact a life similar to the Pararauate Indians.' Directly however, our ancestors spread into temperate climates this mode of life would become impossible and they would be compelled to seek their nourishment, in part at least from the animal kingdom. Then, if not before, the knife and the hammer would develop into the spear and club.

It is too often supposed that the world was peopled by a series of 'migrations'. But migrations properly so called are compatible only with a comparatively high state of organisation. Moreover it has been observed that the geographical distribution of the various races of man curiously coincides with that of the other races of animals; and there can be no doubt that, man originally crept over the earth's surface, little by little, year by year just for instance as the weeds of Europe are now gradually but surely creeping over the surface of Australia.

The preceding argument assumes of course the unity of the human race. It would however be impossible to end this volume without saying a few words on this great question. It must be admitted that the principal varieties of mankind are of great antiquity.

We find on the earliest Egyptian monuments some of which are certainly as ancient as 2,400 BC, 'two great distinct types, the Arab on the east and west of Egypt, and the negroes on the south and the Egyptian type occupying a middle place between the two ...' 'Those who consider length of time can change a type of man, will do well to consider the fact that three thousand years give no ratio on which a calculation could be founded'. I am however not aware that it is supposed by any school of ethnologists that 'time' alone, without a change of external circumstances, will produce an alteration of type ... . But Mr Crawford goes too far when he denies altogether any change of type. In spite of the comparatively short time which has elapsed, and of the immense immigration which has been kept up, there is already a marked difference between the English of Europe and those of America, and it would be desirable to enquire, whether in their own eyes, the Negroes of the New World exactly resemble those of Africa.

But there are some reasons which make it probable that changes of external condition, or rather of country, produce less effect than was formerly the case. At present when men migrate they carry with them the manners and appliances of civilised life. They build houses more or less like those to which they have been accustomed, carry with them their flocks and herds ... . But as we have seen this has not always been the case. When man first spread over the earth, he had no domestic animals, perhaps not even the dog ... his food, habits and whole manner of life must then have varied as he passed from one country to another, he must have been far more subject to the influence of external circumstances, and in all probability more susceptible of change ... . If there is any truth in this view of the subject, it will necessarily follow that the principal varieties of man are of great antiquity, and in fact go back almost to the origins of the human race ...

This argument has been carried still farther by Mr. Wallace in an admirable memoir on 'The Origin of Human Races and the Antiquity of Man deduced from the theory of Natural Selection'. He has attempted to reconcile the two great schools of ethnologists who hold opinions 'so diametrically opposed to each other; the one party positively maintaining that man is a species and essentially one ... . the other party maintaining with equal confidence that man is a genus of many species, each of which is practically unchangeable ...' Mr Wallace himself holds the former of these theories ... and he shows that the true solution of this difficulty lies in the theory of Natural Selection, which with characteristic unselfishness he ascribes to Mr Darwin, although as is well known, he struck out the idea independently and published it, though not with the same elaboration, at the same time.

After explaining the true nature of the theory, which it must be confessed, is even yet very much misunderstood, he points out that as long as man led what may be called an animal existence, he would be subject to the same laws, and would vary in the same manner as the rest of his fellow creatures but at length 'by the capacity of clothing himself, and making weapons and tools (he) has taken away from nature that power of changing the external form and structures which she exercises over all other animals ... . From the time then when the social and sympathetic feelings came into active operation, and the intellectual and moral faculties became fairly developed, man would cease to be influenced by natural selection in his physical form and structure … . But from the moment that his body became stationary, his mind would become subject to those very influences from which his body had escaped; every slight variation in his mental and moral nature which should enable him better to guard against adverse circumstances, and combine for mutual comfort and protection would be preserved and accumulated …, and in conjunction with scarcely perceptible modifications of form, has developed the wonderful intellect of the Germanic races'.

Mr Wallace appears to me to press his arguments a little too far when he says that man is no longer 'influenced by natural selection' and that his body has 'become stationary' …

> 'Here then we see the true grandeur and dignity of man. On this view of his special attributes, we may admit that even those who claim for him a position and an order, a class, or a sub-kingdom by himself, have some reason on their side. He is indeed a being apart, since he is not influenced by the great laws which irresistibly modify all other organic beings. Nay more: this history which he has gained for himself gives him a directing influence over other existences. Man has not only escaped 'natural selection' himself, but he is actually able to take away some of that power from nature which, before his appearance she universally exercised …'

Thus, then, the great principle of Natural Selection, which is to biology what the law of gravitation is for astronomy, not only throws an unexpected light on the past but illuminates the future with hope; nor can I but feel surprised that a theory which thus teaches us humility for the past, faith in the present, and hope for the future, should have been regarded as opposed to the principles of Christianity or the interests of true religion.

But even if the theory of 'natural selection' should eventually prove to be untenable … still I think we are justified in believing that the happiness of man is greatly on the increase. It is generally admitted that if any animal increases in numbers it must be because the conditions are becoming more favourable to it, in other words, because it is happier and more comfortable. Now how will this test apply to man? Schoolcraft estimates that in a population which lives on the produce of the chase, each hunter requires on an average 50,000 acres, or 78 square miles, for his support. Again he tells us that excluding Michigan territory west of Lake Michigan, and north of Illinois there were in the United States, in 1825, about 97,000 Indians occupying 77,000,000 of acres or 120,312 square miles. This gives one inhabitant to every 1.25 square miles. In this case however the Indians lived partly on subsidies granted them by the Government in exchange for land, and the population was therefore greater than would have been the case if they had lived entirely on the produce of the chase. The same reason affects, though to a smaller extent, the Indians of Hudson's Bay territory. These tribes were estimated by Sir George Simpson ..., in 1857, at 139,000, and the extent is supposed to be more than 1,400,000 square miles, to which we must add 13,000 more for Vancouver Island, making a total of more than 900,000,000 of acres; about 6,500 or 10 square miles to each individual. Again, the inhabitants of Patagonia south of 40°, and exclusive of Chile and Tierra del Fuego are estimated by Admiral Fitzroy at less than 4,000, and the number of acres 176,640,000, giving more than 44,000 acres, or 68 square miles for each person. It would be difficult to form any census of the aborigines of Australia; Mr Oldcastle estimates that there is one native for every 50 square miles ...

Indeed population invariably increases with civilisation. Paraguay, with 100,000 square miles has from 300,000 to 500,000 inhabitants or about four to a square mile ... Naples had more than 183 inhabitants to each square mile; Venetia more than 200, Lombardy 280, England 280, Venetia as many as 320.

Finally we cannot but observe that, under civilisation the means of subsistence have increased, even more rapidly than the population. Far from suffering from want of food the more densely peopled countries are exactly those in which it is not only absolutely, but even relatively most abundant. It is said that a man who makes two blades of grass grow where one grew before is a benefactor to the human race; what shall we say of that which enables a thousand men to live in plenty, where one savage could scarcely find a scanty and precarious existence?

There are indeed many who doubt whether happiness is increased by civilisation and who talk of the free and noble savage. But the true savage is neither free nor noble; he is a slave to his own wants, his own passions: imperfectly protected from the weather he suffers from the cold by night and the heat of the sun by day; ignorant of agriculture, living by the chase, and improvident in success, hunger always stares him in the face, and often drives him to the terrible alternative of cannibalism or death.

Wild animals are always in danger. Mr Galton, who is so well qualified to form an opinion, believes that the life of all beasts in their wild state is an exceedingly anxious one. ... So it is with the savage; he is always suspicious, always in danger, always on the watch. He can depend on no one, and no one can depend on him. ... The position of the female savage is even more wretched than that of her master. She not only bears his sufferings, but has to bear his ill-humour and ill-usage ...

Not content however with those incident to their mode of life, savages appear to take a melancholy pleasure in self-inflicted sufferings. Besides the very general practice of tattooing, the most extraordinary methods of disfigurement and self-torture are adopted; some cut off the little finger, some make an immense hole in the under-lip, or pierce the cartilage of the nose. The Easter Islanders enlarge their ears till they reach down to their shoulders; the Chinooks and many other American tribes, alter the shape of their heads; the Japanese that of their feet. Some of the African tribes chip their teeth in various manners ... ... These and many other curious practices are none the less painful because they are voluntary.

If we turn to the bright side of the question the whole analogy of nature justifies us in concluding that the pleasures of civilised man are greater than those of the savage. As we descend in the scale of organisation, we find that animals become more and more vegetative in their characteristics; with less susceptibility to pain, and consequently less capacity for happiness. It may indeed well be doubted whether some of these beings which from their anatomy we are compelled to class as animals, have much more consciousness of enjoyment, or even of existence, than a tree or seaweed ... . Moreover the savage is like a child who sees only that which is brought directly before him, but the civilised man questions nature, and by the various processes of chemistry, by electricity, and magnetism, by a thousand ingenious contrivances, he forces nature to throw light upon himself discovers hidden uses and unsuspected beauties, almost as if he were endowed with some entirely new organ of sense ...

The well-known proverb against looking a gift horse in the mouth does not apply to the gifts of nature; they will bear the closest inspection, and the more we examine the more we shall find to admire. Nor are these new sources of happiness accompanied by any new liability to suffering; on the contrary, while our pleasures are increased, our pains are lessened; in a thousand ways we can avoid or diminish evils which to our ancestors were great and inevitable, How much misery, for instance, has been spared to the human race by the single discovery of chloroform? ...

Thus then with the increasing influence of science, we may confidently look to a great improvement in the condition of man. But it may be said that our present sufferings and sorrows arise principally from sin, and any moral improvement must be due to religion, not to science. This separation of the two mighty agents of improvement is the great misfortune of humanity, and has done more than anything else to retard the progress of civilisation. But even if for the moment we admit that science will not render us more virtuous, it must certainly make us more innocent. Out of 129,000 persons committed to prison in England and Wales during the year 1863, only 4,829 could read and write. In fact our criminal population are mere savages in the midst, and at the expense, of a civilised community.

Men do not sin for the sake of sinning; they yield to temptation. Most of our unhappiness arises from a mistaken pursuit of pleasure; from a misapprehension of that which constitutes true happiness. Men do wrong either from ignorance, or the unexpressed hope that they may enjoy the pleasure and yet avoid the penalty of sin. In this respect there can be no doubt that religious teaching is widely mistaken. Repentance is often regarded as a substitute for punishment. Sin it is thought is followed *either* by one or the other. So far however as our world is concerned this is not the case; repentance may enable a man to avoid punishment in the future, but has no effect on the consequences of the past. The laws of nature are just, and they are salutary, but they are also inexorable ...

May we not however go even further than this, and say also that science will render men more virtuous. 'To pass our time' says Lord Brougham 'in the study of the sciences is learning what others have discovered, and in extending the bounds of human knowledge has in all ages been reckoned the most dignified and happy of human occupations ...'

In reality we are but on the threshold of civilisation. Far from showing any indication of having come to an end the tendency to improvement seems latterly to have proceeded with augmented impetus and accelerated rapidity. Why then should we suppose that it must now cease? Man has surely not reached the limits of his intellectual development, and it is certain that he has not exhausted the infinite capabilities of nature. There are many things which are not as yet dreamt of in our philosophy; many discoveries that will immortalise those who make them and confer upon the human race advantages which as yet, perhaps we are not in a condition to appreciate. We still say with our great countryman, Sir Isaac Newton, that we have been but like children playing on the seashore, and picking up here and there a smoother pebble or a prettier shell than ordinary, while the great ocean of truth lies all undiscovered before us.

Thus, then, the most sanguine hopes for the future are justified by the whole experience of the past. It is surely unreasonable that a process that has been going on for so many thousand years should have now suddenly ceased; and he must be blind indeed who imagines that our civilisation is unsusceptible of improvement, or that we ourselves are in the highest state attainable by man. If we turn from experience to theory, the same conclusion forces itself upon us.

The great principle of natural selection which in animals affects the body and seems to have little influence on the mind; in man affects the mind and has little influence on the body. In the first it tends mainly to the preservation of life; in the second to the improvement of the mind and consequently to the increase of happiness. It ensures in the words of Herbert Spencer, 'a constant progress towards a higher degree of skill, intelligence and self-regulation – a better co-ordination of actions – a more complete life'. Even those however, who are dissatisfied with the reasoning of Mr Darwin, who believe that neither our mental and material organisation are susceptible of any considerable change, may still look forward to the future with hope. The tendency of recent improvements and discoveries is less to effect any rapid change in man himself, than to bring him into harmony with nature; less to confer upon him new powers, than to teach him how to apply the old.

It will, I think, be admitted that of the evils under which we suffer nearly all may be attributed to ignorance or sin. That ignorance will be diminished by the progress of science is of course self-evident that the same will be the case with sin seems less so. Thus then both theory and experience point to the same conclusion. The future happiness of our race, which poets hardly ventured to hope for, science boldly predicts. Utopia which we have long looked upon as synonymous with an evident impossibility which we have ungratefully regarded as 'too good to be true' turns on the contrary to be the necessary consequence of natural laws, and once more we find that the simple truth exceeds the most brilliant flights of imagination.

Even in our own time we may hope to see improvement, but the unselfish mind will find its gratification in the belief that whatever may be the case with ourselves, our descendants will understand many things which are hidden from us now, will better appreciate the beautiful world in which we live, avoid much of that suffering to which we are subject, enjoy many blessings of which we are not yet worthy, and escape many of those temptations which we deplore, but cannot wholly resist.

Appendix 6

List of 100 Books

This list is from the end of chapter 4, pages 89–93 of *The Pleasures of Life, Part 1* (1887), which according to a footnote at the beginning of the chapter was a lecture given at the London Working Men's College, presumably in 1886. The last sentence of the text above reads: 'How thankful we ought to be for these inestimable blessings, for this numberless host of friends who never weary, betray or forsake us!'

List of 100 Books *Works by Living Authors are omitted*

The Bible
The Meditations of Marcus Aurelius
Epictetus
Aristotle's Ethics
Analects of Confucius
St Hilaire's *Le Bouddha et sa Religion*
Wake's Apostolic Fathers
Thos. a Kempis's *Imitation of Christ*
Confessions of St Augustine (Dr Pusey)

The Koran (portions of)

Spinoza's *Tractatus Theologico-Politicus*

Comte's *Catechism of Positive Philosophy*

Pascal's Pensées

Butler's *Analogy of Religion*

Taylor's *Holy Living and Dying*

Bunyan's *Pilgrim's Progress*

Keble's Christian Year

Plato's Dialogue; at any rate, the Apology, Phaedo and Republic

Xenophon's Memorabilia

Aristotle's *Politics*

Demosthenes's *De Corona*

Cicero's *De Officiis, De Amicitia, and De Senectute*

Plutarch's Lives

Berkeley's Human Knowledge

Descartes's *Discours sur la Methode*

Locke's *On the Conduct of the Understanding*

Homer

Hesiod

Virgil

Mahabharata   Epitomised in Tallboys Wheeler's *History of India,* vols i and ii.

Ramayana

The *Shahnameh*

The Nibelungenlied

Malory's *Morte d'Arthur*

The Shaking

Kalidasa's Sakuntala or The Lost Ring

Aeschylus's Prometheus

Trilogy of Orestes

Sophocles's Oedipus

Euripedes's Medea

Aristophanes's *The Knights and the Clouds*

Horace

Chaucer's *Canterbury Tales* (perhaps in Morris's edition or if expurgated, in C. Clarke's or Mrs Haweis's)

Shakespeare
Milton's *Paradise Lost, Lycidas, Comus* and the shorter poems.
Dante's *Divina Commedia*
Spenser's *Faerie Queen*
Dryden's Poems
Scott's Poems
Wordsworth (Mr. Arnold's Selection)
Pope's Essay on Criticism
Essay on Man
Rape of the Lock
Burns
Byron's *Childe Harold*
Gray
Herodotus
Xenophon's *Anabasis and memorabilia*
Thucydides
Tacitus's *Germania*
Livy
Gibbon's *Decline and Fall*
Hume's *History of England*
Grote's *History of Greece*
Carlyle's *French Revolution*
Green's *Short History of England*
Lewes's *History of Philosophy*
Arabian Nights
Swift's *Gulliver's Travels*
Goldsmith's *Vicar of Wakefield*
Cervantes's *Don Quixote*
Boswell's *Life of Johnson*
Molière
Schiller's *William Tell*
Sheridan's *The Critic, School for Scandal, The Rivals*
Carlyle's *Past and Present*
Bacon's *Novum Organum*
Smith's *Wealth of Nations* (part of)
Mill's *Political Economy*

Cook's Voyages

Humboldt's Travels

White's *Natural History of Selborne*

Darwin's *Origin of Species, Naturalist's Voyage*

Mill's Logic

Bacon's Essays

Montaigne's Essays

Hume's Essays

Macaulay's Essays

Addison's Essays

Emerson's Essays

Burke's Select Works

Smiles's Self-Help

Voltaire's *Zadig and Micromegas*

Goethe's *Faust*, and Autobiography

Thackeray's *Vanity Fair, Pendennis*

Dickens's *Pickwick, David Copperfield*

Lytton's *Last Days of Pompeii*

George Eliot's *Adam Bede*

Kingsley's *Westward Ho!*

Scott's Novels

Appendix 7

Three of Lubbock's Essays

All three essays are taken from *Peace and Happiness* (1909), shortened and with footnotes omitted. Some or perhaps all three had originally been given as lectures

A. *Aspiration* (chapter 4, pp. 77–95)

The late Sir James Stephen in a lecture to young men once said that he would put his suggestions in one word – Aspire.

This is very good advice. But what should the aspiration be? Not to grasp at everything! That would be a very unworthy aim: but to raise oneself above oneself—not above others, but as far as possible with others. Those who profess to despise the good opinion of others, seldom deserve it. It is well to aim high lest we fall low. It is impossible not to commit errors but it is quite possible to prevent oneself from doing so. Some people seem to expect that opportunities should find them, instead of them finding opportunities ...

What should our aspirations be? We must think of others as well as ourselves. Being as we are citizens of a great Empire, we may bear in mind the old Athenian oath: 'I will not abandon my sacred shield; I will not abandon my fellow-soldier in the ranks; I will do battle for our altars and our homes, whether aided or unaided; I will leave our country not less but greater and nobler than she is now entrusted to me'.

We may, and indeed we ought, to desire the respect of our countrymen and contemporaries but the craving for glory is a temptation and a danger. 'An inordinate passion for glory,' says Cicero 'as I have already observed, is likewise to be guarded against; for it deprives us of liberty, the only prize for which men of elevated sentiments ought to contend. Power is so far from being desirable in itself, that it sometimes ought to be refused and sometimes to be resigned ... .'

Many envy the rich and powerful. They are supposed to be fortunate that they can buy what they like and do what they wish. But to be fortunate is not necessarily to be happy. In hunting it is not the kill but the chase which is the fascination. The satisfaction of rising is greater than that of having risen. If we had nothing to wish for, nothing to aspire to, half the zest and interest of life would be gone.

Those who are 'born to the purple' have indeed many advantages, but they pay dearly for them. They have little to wish for and much to fear. Not only is their time—their precious time—frittered away in endless and tedious ceremonials involving constant dressing and undressing, and interminable interviews, levees, reviews, council meetings, public meetings, public or semi-public dinners and deputations; not only must they be on their guard against flatterers, and against even more temptations that assail those less eminent, but their cares weigh heavily on them. 'Uneasy', says Shakespeare, 'the head that wears a crown' ... 'Princes are like heavenly bodies, which cause good or evil times, and which have much veneration, but no rest' (Bacon).

> ... and the lesson which Dionysius of Syracuse gave to Damocles applies to most monarchs, and indeed to some degree to most men. Moreover, as Bacon says, 'He that is used to go forward and findeth a stop, falleth out of his own favour, and is not the thing he was'.

... It has been well said that force is no remedy; those are mistaken who hope in the words of Sadi, 'by the strength of their arm to grasp the skirt of their wishes'. Moreover if rising is anxious, falling is painful, and many in the words of Milton

Rather than to be less
Cared not to be at all

Those who are on a pinnacle are always in danger of catastrophe. We all know how dizzy it is to stand on a precipice ...

It may be true though I doubt it, that

One crowded hour of glorious life
is worth an age without a name (Scott)

and it is a grand thing to

Ride on a whirlwind and direct a storm (Addison)

Still one may buy gold too dear, and 'it is a bad bargain to lose control over one's actions and time, in order to gain power over others; it is a strange desire to seek power and lose liberty; to seek power over others and to lose power over oneself'. Madame de Stael described fame as 'a splendid mourning for happiness' though as in so many other cases she did not herself act upon her own advice ...

Moreover riches, honours and power unfit a man for enjoying some of the true blessings of life. While deprecating ambition there is a despairing regret in Wolsey's lament

Farewell! a long farewell to all my greatness!
This is the state of man; today he puts forth
The tender leaves of hope; tomorrow blossoms ...

Those whose aspiration is for power cannot hope for peace and those who wish for a quiet and peaceful life must not look for greatness. 'Non est ad astra mollis a terris via' (Seneca) ...

Moreover, 'you need not be solicitous about power, nor strive after it. If you be wise and good it will follow you though you should not wish it'. It is better to stand on the solid rock of virtue than on the slippery and fragile ice of fortune. Success in almost any career requires hard work. It is not to be acquired by sudden rushes and spasmodic exertions. Quiet, steady and determined perseverance is the necessary condition of progress. The Alpine climber scales the mountain by firm, steady steps, without haste but without faltering ...

If you cannot leave wealth or a high station to your children, you can at least leave them a good name. 'If therefore a man is unable to defend causes, to entertain the people by haranguing, or to wage war yet still he ought to do what is in his power. ... Now, the best inheritance a parent can leave a child—more excellent than any patrimony—is the glory of his virtue and his deeds; to bring disgrace on which ought to be regarded as wicked and monstrous'. (Cicero) ...

Socialists generally defend their policy by the argument that the present state of things is unsatisfactory and indefensible. But we may feel this without being Socialists. Socialism is fatal to individual enterprise and to freedom, as an economical problem it is foredoomed to failure. It would check production and thus reduce the supply of food and other necessaries. But what is worse is that it implies implicit submission to the decrees of the State, ie of State officials. What led to the tyranny and eventual ruin of the Roman and other Empires? ... . We cannot therefore look for improvement in that direction. But I believe we shall avoid these dangers, and am firmly convinced that the world will still advance.

The ancients seem to have no idea of progress. They pictured the Golden Age as in the past. We hope and believe that it is in the future ... . Our main progress has been due to observation and experiment. We have gone to our Mother Nature and she has taught us.

It is sad no doubt when, in Huxley's words 'an ugly fact kills a beautiful hypothesis'. We may mourn but we must bury it. Thoughts wear like money ... . But gradually it is worn with use, and, as Macaulay said 'a point which yesterday was unseen is its goal today, and will be its starting point tomorrow'.

The progress of science in the last century has been simply marvellous. It has allowed us not only to weigh and measure but even to analyse the stars; to descend to the recesses of the earth and the abysses of the ocean. ... it has relieved suffering and found remedies for pain; it has lengthened life and added immensely to the interest of existence; to it we owe our knowledge of bygone ages and the very idea of progress in the future.

Renan has described the last as the most amusing century. I should rather have described it as most interesting, full of unexpected and far-reaching discoveries and inventions: railways and steamers, telegraphs and photography, petroleum and electric light ... the liquefaction of air and even of hydrogen, the far-reaching discoveries of Darwin, the foundation of geology, the discovery of anaesthetics and the antiseptic treatment, constitute a glorious galaxy of marvellous discoveries. And what is true of material or physical remains holds good with equal force in the realms of theory and of morals ...

This being so we cannot but ask ourselves whether the century which is now commencing is likely to endow us with results so far reaching. The late Lord Derby—certainly one of our wisest statesman—thought that this could not be hoped; but though I differ from so great an authority with much hesitation, still I cannot help thinking that there are strong reasons for looking forward to the future with hope. If indeed the world was fairly well known to us, if our knowledge bore any considerable proportion to what we do not yet know the case would be different. But what we do know is an absolutely infinitesimal fraction of what we do not know, there is no single substance in Nature the uses and properties of which are yet completely known to us ... . Then amongst others there are three special reasons which seem fully to justify the hopes that inspire me. In the first place the continual improvement in our instruments and apparatus, and the invention of new instruments of research; secondly the increased number of workers, though we may still say that the harvest is truly plenteous but the labourers are few; and thirdly, that as the sunshine of discovery bursts through the clouds of ignorance, as the bright light of science pierces through the mist and mystery which surrounds us, with the continually increasing circle of light, so the possibilities of progress are continually increasing. Every discovery which is made suggests fresh lines of inquiry, opens the door and paves the way to still more marvellous and unexpected triumphs.

Our children are now commencing their career under eminent teachers, and have great advantages and opportunities; most, sincerely do I hope, and indeed believe, that in the triumphal progress of science which I foresee – which they, I hope, will see, many of them and some, I trust, of those nearest and dearest to me, may take an honourable part, and add to the sum of human knowledge. 'Science has lengthened life; it has mitigated pain; it has extinguished diseases; it has increased the fertility of the soil; it has given new security to the mariner; it has spanned great rivers and estuaries with bridges of form unknown to our forefathers ... it has enabled man to descend to the depths of the sea, to soar into the sky, to penetrate surely into the noxious recesses of the earth, to traverse the land in cars which whirl along without horses ...'. (Macaulay).

'Truth', says Milton, 'is compared in Scripture to a streaming fountain; if her waters flow not in a perpetual progression, they sicken into a sickly pond of conformity and tradition' ...

Science is of vital importance in our life; it is more fascinating than a fairy tale, more brilliant than a novel and any one who neglects to follow the triumphant march of discovery ... is deliberately rejecting one of the greatest comforts and interests of life, one of the greatest gifts with which we have been endowed by Providence ...

But what is progress? It does not consist in the increase of exports and imports, commerce and machinery, railways and telegraphs; still less in conquests and annexations. The true prosperity of a nation does not depend on any of these things; but in the increase in the healthiness, happiness worthiness of the human beings of which it is composed; and it is a blessed privilege and a high aspiration that we may all in life contribute in some measure to this noble object.

B. NOW (Chapter 13, pp. 265–276)

> Boast not thyself of tomorrow; for thou knowest not what
> the day may bring forth.—*Proverbs*
> There is a tide in the affairs of men
> Which, taken at the flood, leads on to fortune
> Omitted, all the voyage of their life
> Is bound in shallows and in miseries—Shakespeare
> The past is gone, the future may never come, the present
> is our own
> Now says Thomas à Kempis in *The Imitation of Christ*
> Now is the time to act.
> Now is the time to fight
> Now is the time to make myself a better man
> If today you are not ready
> Will you be to-morrow?
> To-morrow may never come as far as you are concerned.

Do not act as if you had a thousand years to live. Delay is always dangerous. What is well begun is half done. What is once put off is more difficult than before. Even:

> Youth is not rich in time; it may be poor;
> Part with it as with money, sparing; pay
> No moment but in purchase of its worth
> And what its worth, ask death-beds—they can tell
> Even the years of Methusaleh came to an end at last.
> Pulvis et umbra sumus
> Quis scit an adidant hoderniae crastina summae
> Tempora di superi! (Horace)

Thrift of time is as important, or rather more important than that of money. The Bible urges this over and over again. 'teach me to number my days' said Moses ... 'Sufficient to the day' said Christ 'is the evil thereof'—sufficient but not intolerable.

Many are the proverbs inculcating prompt action. 'Strike while the iron is hot' ... Many are more or less melancholy:

All pleasures are like poppies spread
You seize the flower, the bloom is shed;
Or like the snowfalls on the river,
A moment white—then melt for ever

And again

PEU DE CHOSE
La vie est vaine
Un peu d'amour
Un peu de haine
Et puis—bon jour!

La vie est brève
Un peu d'espoir
Un peu de rêve.
Et puis—bon jour

'The world's a bubble' says Bacon 'and the life of man less than a span.'

Like the dew on the mountain,
Like the foam on he river
Like the bubble on the fountain
Thou art gone, and for ever (Scott) ...

'Enjoy the blessings' says Jeremy Taylor 'of this day if God send them, and the evils of it bear patiently and sweetly; for this day is only ours; we are dead to yesterday, and we are not born to the tomorrow. He therefore that enjoys the present, if it be good, enjoys as much as possible, and if only that day's trouble leans upon him, it is singular and finite'.

'If a man' said Bishop Fuller, 'chance to die young, yet he lives long that lives well; a time misspent is not lived but lost'. Moreover if you lose any of your time, you will hardly find it again. Yet while all men cling to life many are often dull and at a loss what to do with their time

... '. Lord Chesterfield said that the Duke of Newcastle lost an hour in the morning and spent the rest of the day looking for it. It is important to arrange every day so as to dovetail duties as well as we can. If we do not much valuable time is lost and though it is altogether our own fault, we are apt to complain with Benjamin Constant 'How I lose my time! What an unarrangeable life is mine!' ...

When we have a number of duties to perform it is sometimes difficult to know where to begin. Perhaps the best rule is to take the most unpleasant first. What is disagreeable in prospect is often pleasant to look back on. Youth has been compared to a garland of roses, age to a crown of thorns. Shakespeare expresses the general feeling, perhaps, when he tells us that

> Youth is full of pleasure
> Age is full of care!
> Youth, I do adore thee;
> Age, I do abhor thee

In youth it may be natural to be anxious. They have had little experience of the world; if unfortunately they have not good guidance they may make great mistakes; life is before them; if they are rash and unwise in a moment of haste they bring on themselves years of trouble. In old age, on the other hand, if we have been wise when young, we have friends, we have earned our rest and misfortunes cannot affect us long ...

Time is kind to those who use it well. As Joubert says, 'Il detruit tout avec lenteur; il mine, il use, il déracine, il détache, et n'arrache pas'. Too many however so arrange their life like a day that breaks in beauty and ends in storm ...

.... Bishop Taylor tells us: 'This day alone is ours; we are dead to yesterday, and we are not yet born tomorrow'. 'Today,' says Schopenhauer, 'comes only once and never returns.' Seneca took a more cheerful view, 'Times past,' he said, 'we make our own by remembrance, the present by use and the future by providence and foresight.' The difficulty is to combine prudence with decision. It is not marriage only that may be undertaken in haste and regretted at leisure; but on the other hand,

'He that observeth the wind shall not sow, and he that regardeth the clouds shall not reap.' (Ecclesiastes, xi, 4).

There is a certain tendency to deprecate the time in which we live. Ruskin for instance though generally grateful and appreciative when speaking of the nineteenth century, that interesting and progressive century, said that he looked forward with longing to the time when 'this disgusting century has – I cannot say breathed, but steamed its last'.

Poets have a great tendency to melancholy and lamentation. It is no doubt true that

Not even Jove upon the past has power (Young): Time is invaluable and irrevocable.

C. The Peace of Nations (Chapter 18, pp. 361–86)

Non exercitus, neque thesauri, praesidia regni sunt, verum amici (Sallust)

(The Safety of a country does not consist in arms or in Wealth but in friends).

The present state of Europe is a danger and even a disgrace to us all. There may be some excuse for barbarous tribes who settle their disputes by force of arms, but that civilised nations should do so is not only repugnant to our moral, but also to our common, sense. At present even the peace establishments of Europe comprise 4,000,000 men; the war establishments are over 10,000,000, and when the proposed arrangements are completed will exceed 20,000,000 men. The nominal cost is over £250,000,000 annually, but as Continental armies are to a great extent under conscription, the actual cost is far larger. Moreover, if these 4,000,000 men were usefully employed and taking the value of their labour only at £50 a year, we must add another £200,000,000, bringing up the total expenditure of Europe on military and naval matters to over £450,000,000 a year!

It is no doubt difficult, not to say impossible, to compare exactly the forces or expenditure of different countries. The different conditions of military service, the division into regular army, militia, volunteers, reserves, *Landwehr*, on the one hand, and the different modes of keeping accounts on the other, interpose insuperable difficulties and the comparison can only be approximate. This is however the less material as the problem is not a question of detail.

The following table shows the military and naval forces of the United States and the so-called 'peace' establishment of the principal States of Europe:–

Country	Men under Arms	Annual cost
United Kingdom	420,000	£65,000,000
Russia	1,150,000	£46,500,000
Germany	661,000	£43,800,000
France	620,000	£41,000,000
Austria-Hungary	384,000	£19,400,000
Italy	305,000	£17,000,000
Spain	100,000	£6,700,000
Norway and Sweden	73,000	£5,500,000
Turkey	370,000	£4,800,000
Holland	35,000	£3,650,000
Belgium	50,000	£2,500,000
Portugal	34,000	£2,600,000
Switzerland	148,000	£1,300,000
Greece	23,000	£1,200,000
Denmark	14,000	£1,200,000
Bulgaria	43,000	£1,000,000
United States	107,000	£40,000,000

Even the gigantic waste of human labour and human life does not satisfy the cravings of ambition and we are incessantly called on for more ships and bigger armies. Of course there are deeper and graver considerations than questions of money, yet money represents human labour and human life.

It is impossible for any one to contemplate the present naval and military arrangements without the gravest forebodings; even if they do not lead to war they will eventually end in bankruptcy and ruin. The principal countries of Europe are running deeper and deeper into debt … . Taking the Government debts of the world together they amounted in 1870 to £4,000,000,000 a fabulous, terrible and crushing weight. But what are they now? They have risen to over £6,000,000,000, and are still increasing.

A Japanese statesman is reported to have said that as long as his countrymen only sent us beautiful works of art, we in Europe regarded them as a semi-barbarous people; now that they have shot down many thousand Russians, we recognise them as a truly civilised nation!

We are told that each nation must protect its own interests; but the greatest interest of every nation is Peace. In thinking of war we are too apt to remember only the pomp and ceremony, the cheerful music, brilliant uniforms and arms glittering in the sunshine, and to forget the bayonets dripping with blood. The carnage and suffering which war entails are terrible to contemplate. It is impossible to read the history of the Russo-Japanese War, or for that matter of any war, without a feeling of intense compassion and horror.

Moreover all wars are unsuccessful. The only question is which of the combatants suffers most. 'Nothing,' said the Duke of Wellington, 'except a battle lost can be half as melancholy as a battle won.' Nothing is so ruinous to a country as a successful war, excepting of course one that is unsuccessful.

'Where Legions are quartered, briars and thorns grow. In the track of great armies there must follow bad years.' (Lau-Tsze). Victor Cousin, in his introduction to *History of Philosophy* designates war as the terrible, indeed, but necessary instrument of civilisation which he says is founded on two rocks, 'le champ de bataille ou la solitude du cabinet'. Surely it would be more correct to say that the horrors of war are continually counteracting the blessings of peace and thought. Victory is only defeat in disguise. Milton says:

Who overcomes
By force, hath overcome but half his foe

And to quote a great German writer, Schiller justly tells us that the enemy who is overcome will rise again, but he who is reconciled is truly vanquished. 'Ce qui vient par la guerre' says Joubert, 's'en retournera par la guerre; toute dépouille sera reprisé; tout butin sera dispersé; tous les vainquers seront vaincus, et la toute ville pleine de proie sera saccagée à son tour'. History proves the truth of Joubert's aphorisms. Where are the great military monarchies?

Are there not troubles and dangers and anxieties enough in life without creating others for ourselves. The poor we always have with us; bad seasons and poor harvests we must expect; changes of climate, failures of mines, new discoveries, fluctuations of commerce, even changes of fashion, may involve heavy losses and much suffering, but the worst misfortunes of all are those which nations bring on themselves. 'Il semble', says Joubert, 'que les peuples aiment les périls, et lorsqu'ils en manquent, ils s'en créent'

Happily however of late years a strong conviction has been growing up, both here and on the Continent, that efforts should be made to create better relations between the nations of Europe. This is no mere matter of sentiment ... no; it is a matter of absolute necessity, as we shall find out sooner or later and the sooner the better for us all. We talk of foreign countries but in fact there are no really foreign countries. The interests of nations are so interwoven, we are bound together by such strong, if sometimes almost invisible threads, that if one suffers all suffer; if one flourishes it is good for the rest.

Europe has immense investments all over the world; our merchants are in all lands; we have built railways and factories in almost every country ... . In Argentina alone our investments amount to more than £150,000. It may almost be said to be an English colony ...

We do not, I think, realise how greatly we are interested in the prosperity of foreign countries ... . Then again if the world's harvests are good our people get their bread for less and their wages go further; if there are good rains in Australia, woollens are cheaper.

In the Crimean War our fleet went to the Baltic and burnt a considerable quantity of Russian produce; that is to say it was produced in Russia. But whose property was it? Much of it belonged to English merchants and was insured in English fire offices. Take again the depredations of the *Alabama*. We paid £3,000,000 [sic] for the damage done to American shipping; that is to say shipping under the American flag. But that very shipping was much of it insured in English insurance companies. The company of which I am a director had to pay many thousands …

Lord Derby (the 15th Earl) once said that the greatest of British interests was peace. And so it is; not merely that we should be at peace ourselves but that other countries should be at peace also. It is not however only our greatest interest, it is the greatest interest of every country.

> … Only a few years ago the feeling between England and France was very bitter, owing mainly to newspaper articles doing fiends' work and creating ill-will. Thanks to wiser counsels, these misunderstandings have been cleared away and a better and happier state of things exists …

More recently a similar estrangement which however was not so acute or widespread had been growing between England and Germany. That is or ought to be at an end … . At Berlin, at Cologne, at Frankfurt, at Hamburg, at Munich and elsewhere—in fact at all the great commercial centres of Germany—meetings have been held and resolutions passed expressing the warm desire to maintain not only peace but friendship with this country …

The present opportunity, then, seems very favourable for a reduction in armaments … a recent and interesting article on European navies gives the relative effective strength of the English, French and German navies as being at present

TONNAGE

	British	French	German
Battleships	769,900	249,500	230,000
Armoured Cruisers	280,000	148,100	55,700
	1,050,500	397,600	285,700

... He then considers the programme of the three Admiralties and shows that if they are carried out the results will be

TONNAGE

	British	French	German
Battleships	1,119,000	384,000	533,000
Armoured cruisers	809,000	395,000	221,000
	1,928,000	779,000	744,000

Thus then, if the programme is carried out we shall all have been put to enormous expense, and our relative forces will remain almost as they were ...

We are not of course, prepared ourselves, nor do we ask or expect other countries to neglect their own interests or to surrender their own rights ... . the different nations of Europe should conduct themselves as friends and neighbours, as gentlemen and not as brigands, as Christians and not as pirates ...

It is said that 'si vis pacem, para bellum', there is no doubt some truth in this as regards any particular country, but as regards Europe as a whole it is equally certain that these gigantic armaments are a danger to peace, and indefinitely increase the risk of war.

Moreover, a comparison of Europe and America suggests very serious considerations. Commercial competition is world-wide. Now Europe even in peace has 4,000,000 men under arms, and devotes annually over £250,000,000 to naval and military expenditure. The United States of America have 107,000 men in their army and navy, costing £40,000,000. The population of the United States is about 90,000,000, that of Europe about 350,000,000. Thus with, in round numbers, about four times the population we have in the disunited States of Europe about forty times as many men under arms as the United States of America. In fact, on one side of the Atlantic are the United States of America, on the other a number of separate States, not only not united, but in some cases hostile, torn by jealousies and suspicions, hatred and ill will—armed to the teeth and more or less encumbered, like medieval knights, by their own armour ...

The late Mr. E. Atkinson, the eminent American economist, said: 'The burden of national taxation and militarism in the competing countries of Europe, all of which must come out of the annual product, is so much greater that by comparison the United States can make a greater profit of about 5 per cent on the entire annual product before the cost of militarism and the heavy taxes of the European competitors have been defrayed ... .' I do not say that the United States are employing their time and manhood to the best advantage. Their fiscal system is devised to check the use and cultivation of their millions—not of paltry acres, but of square miles of virgin soil, in order to encourage the development of manufactures which they could purchase more economically from us; they endeavour to divert their people from the natural and healthy life of the country, and concentrate them in the great cities. These mistakes, no doubt, are retarding—they cannot prevent the progress of the country.

But what are we doing in Europe? We have no doubt some great advantages. But Europe ought to make hay while the sun shines. We have no reserves of virgin soil. Our coal will not be exhausted just yet, but we have to go deeper and deeper for it so that it becomes more expensive ... . Under these circumstances we ought to be laying up for the future.

So far from this Europe is a great military camp always under arms; we have no peace, only an armistice; eternal war with unlimited expenditure, though happily without bloodshed, but the result is that instead of accumulating capital for our children we are piling up debt; instead of bequeathing them an income we are leaving them overwhelming responsibilities.

It is obvious therefore that our European manufactures are heavily handicapped as against those of the United States and unless something is done will be so more and more. Moreover the unrest in Europe, the spread of socialism, the ominous rise of anarchism, is a warning to the Governments and governing classes that the condition of the working classes in Europe is becoming intolerable, and that if revolution is to be avoided steps must be taken to increase wages, reduce the hours of labour, and lower the prices of the necessaries of life. These objects can be best effected by reducing the military and naval expenditure.

Europe has to consider not merely the direct but the indirect effect of these enormous armaments. The anxiety and uncertainty which are created necessarily tend to paralyse industry and drive manufacture into more peaceful regions.

The naval and military expenditure of the United States and of our Colonies is so small compared with ours and that of other European States that competition with them is becoming more and more difficult. Manufactures will, *ceteris paribus,* gradually be transferred to the countries which are most lightly taxed. This will more and more aggravate the evil, so that unless we turn over a new leaf the prospects of Europe are very grave. In fact, as long as these armaments are maintained we are sitting on a volcano.

The sufferings and hardships of the working classes—sufferings which cannot be reduced so long as the present expenditure is maintained—are leading to a rapid development of socialism. Socialism, I fear, would only aggravate the evil, but it is the protest of the masses against their hard lot. Unless something is done the condition of the poor in Europe will grow worse and worse. It is no use shutting our eyes. Revolution may not come soon, not probably in our time, but come it will, and as sure as fate there will be an explosion such as the world has never seen. If the monarchs of Europe are to retain their thrones, and if we are to maintain peace European statesmen must devise some means of fostering better feelings, and diminishing the burdens which now press so heavily on the springs of industry, and aggravate so terribly the unavoidable troubles of life.

Many countries, again, attempt to make war on one another, almost as foolishly, by fiscal restrictions.

Our poet Cowper observes that—

> Mountains interposed
> make enemies of nations, who had else
> Like kindred drops been mingled into one

But the worst barriers are those which nations have themselves raised against one another—barriers of duties and customs and worst of all unfounded jealousies and suspicions or ill-will each attributing to the other injurious designs, which neither of them perhaps in reality entertain.

In the first place most European countries raise against themselves artificial barriers to progress by their protective duties. This does not apply to us, or to one or two other countries—Holland for instance. The United States also have, unfortunately for themselves, adopted a protective and retrograde policy as regards the outside world, while between the States themselves, from Canada on the north to Mexico on the south, absolute Free trade prevails. The logic is not apparent ...

Is this desire for more friendly relations hopeless? Europe has great interests in common. The late Marquis of Salisbury when Unionist Prime Minister, in a speech delivered at the Mansion House on the 10th of November 1897 made the following remarkable statement: 'But remember this—that the Federation of Europe is the embryo of the only possible structure of Europe which can save civilisation from the desolating effects of a disaster of war. You notice that on all sides the instruments of destruction, the piling up of arms, are becoming larger and larger. The powers of concentration are becoming greater, the instruments of death more active and more numerous and are improved with every year; and each nation is bound, for its own safety's sake to take part in this competition and the one hope that we have to prevent this competition from ending in a terrible effort of self-destruction which would be fatal to Christian civilisation, the one hope that we have is that the powers may gradually be brought together to act in a friendly spirit on all questions of difference ... .'.

Sir Henry Campbell Bannerman, the late Radical Prime Minister of Great Britain, in a speech delivered in London on the 22nd of December, 1905 said, 'In the case of Germany, I see no cause whatever of estrangement in any of the interests of either people and we welcome the unofficial demonstrations of friendship ... I hold that the growth of armaments is a great danger to the peace of the world. The policy of huge armaments feeds the belief that force is the best, if not the only, solution to national differences ... . What nobler role could this great country have than at the fitting moment to place itself at the head of a League of Peace, through whose instrumentality this great work could be effected!'

> ... The present state of Europe is a disgrace to us not only as men of common sense, but as being altogether inconsistent with any form of religious conviction. Unfortunately, there are still some, both in Parliament and in the Press, who make it their business to sow suspicions, magnify differences, to inflame the passions and stir up strife between nations, and the result of their baneful activity is that bloodshed constitutes so much of human history ...

In ancient times every man was a law unto himself. He avenged his own wrongs. Now we do not permit this. Private revenge is treated and justly treated as a crime. He must appeal for protection and redress to the laws of the country.

Is not the time coming, has it not come, when the same should be extended to countries, when they also should be expected to abstain from private vengeance and to appeal to the law of nations? Nations are no better judges in their own cause than individuals: they should not resort to the barbarous expedient of force ...

On all accounts, then, it is most important, may I say it is an imperative duty that we should endeavour to avoid international misunderstandings, and to strengthen friendly feelings between the great nations of the earth. A reduction of armaments would be an enormous boon to the whole world, and especially to the people of Europe; it would I believe save the Continent from drifting into revolution and misery ... . Of course it is possible that our overtures will be rejected. But even if they are we shall feel that we have done our best. We shall have held out the olive branch; but it will be a failure, but an honourable, even glorious failure. I do not however entertain such a fear. I have too much confidence in the common sense and conscience of Europe. And if this policy should happily succeed in replacing extravagance, jealousy, and suspicion by economy, peace and goodwill, it will be one of those cases in which peace has its victories as well as war, and it will confer a incalculable boon not only on the people of Europe but on the whole world. Then, but only then may we reasonably hope that Europe may have a bright and prosperous future before it; and the highest ambition that any nation can place before itself is that it may take a foremost place in the noble work of promoting 'peace on earth and good will amongst men'.

Bibliography

Adams, W. Y. 1998. *The Philosophical Roots of Anthropology*, Stamford.

Armstrong, Patrick, 2000. *The English Parson-Naturalist: a Companionship between Science and Religion*, Leominster.

Auburn, Giles St 1958, *A Victorian Eminence, the Life and Work of Henry Thomas Buckle*.

Bachofen, J., 1841, *Das Mutterrecht*.

Bagehot, Walter, 1872, *Physics and Politics or Thoughts on the Application of the Principles of 'Natural Selection' and 'Inheritance' to Political Society*, London.

Beer, Gavin de (ed.), 1974, Charles Darwin and T. H. Huxley, Autobiographies, Cambridge.

Bowden, M., 1991, *Pitt Rivers*, Cambridge.

Browne, Janet, 2002, *Charles Darwin*. London.

Burkhardt, F and Matt, S. (ed.), 1985, *The Correspondence of Charles Darwin*. In progress, Cambridge

Burrow, J.W., 1970, *Evolution and Society: a Study in Victorian Social Theory*.

Carhart, Michael C., 2007, *The Science of Culture in Enlightenment Germany*, Harvard.

Cassis, Youssef, 1984, *Les Banquiers de la Cité à l'Epoque Edwardienne*, Geneva, Librairie Droz.

Chambers, Robert, 1844, *Vestiges of the Natural History of Creation*, London.

Chippendale, C., 1983, 'The Making of the First Ancient Monuments Act, 1882, and its Administration under General Pitt-Rivers', *Journal of the British Archaeological Association*, 136, pp. 1–55.

Chitty, Susan, 1974, *The Beast and the Monk; a Life of Charles Kingsley*.

Choay, Françoise (trans.), 2001. *The invention of the Historic Monument*.

Clarek, John F. W., 1997, '"The Ants were duly Visited", making sense of John Lubbock, scientific naturalism and the senses of social insects'. *British Journal for the History of Science*, 30, pp. 151–76.

Clark, J. G. D. and Thompson, M. W., 1953, 'The Grove and Splinter Technique of Working Antler in Upper Palaeolithic and Mesolithic Europe', *Proceedings of the Prehistoric Society*, 19, Pt. 2, pp. 148–60

Daniel, G. E., 1943, *The Three Ages*, Cambridge.

Daniel, G. E., 1953, *A Hundred Years of Archaeology*.

Darwin, Charles Robert, 1859, *On the Origin of Species*, 2nd ed. Oxford, 1947.

Darwin, Emma, MS Diary in Cambridge University Library.

Eliegard, Alvar, 1958, *Darwin and the General Reader, the Reception of Darwin's Theory of Evolution in the British Periodical Press, 1859–72*, Gothenberg.

Evans, Sir John, 1872 and 1897, *The Ancient Stone Implements, Weapons, Onaments of Great Britain*, London.

Evans, Sir John, 1881, *The Ancient Bronze Implements of Great Britain*.

Fergusson, J., 1868, *Fire and serpent Worship from the Sculptures of the Buddhist Tepes of Senli and Amravati*.

Fortes, M, 1969, *Kinship and the Social Order.*

Fyfe, Aileen and Lightman, Bernard (ed.), *Science in the Market Place: Nineteenth Century Sites and Experiences*, Chicago.

Grant Duff, Adrian (ed.), 1924 and 1934. *The Life-Work of Lord Avebury (Sir John Lubbock), 1834–1913*, London.

Grant Duff, Sir E. N., *Notes from a diary, 1851–1905*, 14 vols.

Hearnshaw, F. J. C., 1933, *The Social and Political Ideas of Some Representative Thinkers of the Victorian Age*, London.

Hutchinson, H. G., 1914, *Life of Sir John Lubbock, Lord Avebury*, 2 vols.

Huxley, Leonard, 1903, *Life and Letters of Thomas Henry Huxley*, 3 vols, London.

Kains-Jackson, C., 1880, *Our Ancient Monuments and the land around them*, with a Preface by Sir John Lubbock.

Klemm, Gustav, 1843–5, *Allgemeine Culturgeschichte der Menscheit nach der besten Quellen*, 10 vols., Leipzig.

Klemm, Gustav, 1855, *Allgemeine Culturwissenschaft*, 5 vols. (intended)

Klemm, Gustav, 1855, *Einleitung: das Feuer, Nahrung, Getracten, Narcotikia.*

Lartet, E. and Christy, H., 1865–75, *Reliquiae Aquitanicae, being contributions to the archaeology of Perigord.*

Levine, George, 2006, *Darwin Loves You: Natural Selection and the Re-Enchantment of the World*, Princeton.

Levine, Philippa, 1986, *The Amateur and the Professional: Antiquarians, Historians and Archaeologists in Victorian England, 1838–1886.*

Levy-Bruhl, L., 1903, *The Philosophy of Auguste Comte*, London.

Lightman, Bernard, 2007, *Victorian Popularisers of Science*, Chicago.

Lubbock, Sir John, Lord Avebury, (for his books see Appendix 1)

Lubbock, Sir John, Lord Avebury, 1877, 'On the Imperial Policy of Great Britain', *The Nineteenth Century*, 1, pp. 37–49

Lubbock, Sir John, Lord Avebury, 1877, 'On the Preservation of our Ancient National Monuments', *The Nineteenth Century*, 1, pp. 257–269.

Lyell, Sir Charles, 1830–33, *Principles of Geology, being an Attempt to Explore the former Changes of the Earth's Surface'*, 3 vols. Reprinted 1990.

Lyell, Sir Charles, 1863, *The Geological Evidences of the Antiquity of Man with Remarks on the Origin of Species by Variation*, London.

MacLennan, John F. 1865, *Primitive Marriage, an Inquiry into the Origin of the form of capture in Marriage Ceremonies*.

Maine, Henry S., 1861, *Ancient Law: its Connection with the early history of Society and its relation to modern Ideas*.

Marett, R. A., 1956, *Tylor, Modern Sociologists*, London.

Morgan, Lewis H., 1877, *Ancient Society; Researches in the Lines of Human Progress from Savagery through Barbarism to Civilisation*.

Munro, Robert. 1890, *The Lake Dwellings of Europe*.

Natural History Review, 1861–65, 5 vols. published.

Newman, J., 1969, *West Kent and the Weald*, Pevsner's Buildings of England.

Nilsson, Sven, 1868, *The Primitive Inhabitants of Scandinavia. An Essay of Comparative Ethnography, and a Contribution to the History of the Development of Mankind: containing a description of the implements, dwellings, tombs and mode of living of the savages in the north of Europe during the Stone Age. 3rd edition, edited and with an Introduction by Sir John Lubbock, Bart.*

O'Connor, Ralph, 2007, *The Earth on Show: Fossils and the Poetics of Popular Science, 1802–1856*, Chicago.

Patton, Mark, 2007, *Science, Politics and Business in the Work of Sir John Lubbock*. Ashgate.

Pitt-Rivers, General A. H., 1887–96, *Excavations in Cranborne Chase*, 4 vols, privately printed.

Pitt-Rivers, General A. H. L. F., 1906, *The Evolution of Culture and other Essays*, edited by J. L. N. Myers.

Prestwich, Joseph, 1859, 'On the Occurrence of Flint Implements associated with the Remains of Extinct Mammalia', *Proceedings of the Royal Society of London*, 10, pp. 50–59.

Read, Sir H. and Smith, R. S., 1905, 'On a Collection of Antiquities from the Early Iron Age Cemetery of Halstatt presented to the British Museum by the second Lord Avebury', *Archaeologia*, 67, p. 145.

Scarre, C. (ed.), 2005, *The Human Past – World Prehistory and the Development of Human Societies*, London.

Smart, P. E., 1979, 'A Victorian Polymath, Sir John Lubbock', *Journal of the Institute of Bankers*, 4, pp. 144–46.

Spencer, Herbert, 1860, *A System of Philosophy* (started 1860).

Spencer, Herbert, 1884, 'Religion: a Retrospect and Prospect', *The Nineteenth Century* 15, pp. 1–12.

Spencer, Herbert, 1904, *An Autobiography*, 2 vols.

Stocking, George, 1987, *Victorian Anthropology*.

Stocking, George, 1996, *After Tylor, British Social Anthropology*.

Sully, James, 1884, 'Scientific Optimism', *The Nineteenth Century*, 10, pp. 573–587.

Thompson, M. W., 1953, PhD. thesis in Cambridge University Library, entitled *Some Mesolithic Cultures of the Iberian Peninsula*.

Thompson, M. W. 1954, 'Azilian Harpoons', *Proceedings of the Prehistoric Society*, 20, Pt 2, pp. 193–211.

Thompson, M. W., 1960, 'The first Inspector of Ancient Monuments in the field', *Journal of the British Archaeological Association*, 23, pp. 103–24.

Thompson, M. W., 1977, *General Pitt-Rivers, Evolution and Archaeology in the Nineteenth Century*, Bradford on Avon.

Thompson, M. W. and Colin Renfrew 1999, 'The Catalogues of the Pitt-Rivers Museum, Farnham, Dorset', *Antiquity*, 73, pp. 377–93.

Thompson, M. W., 2006, *Ruins Reused, changing attitudes to ruins since the late eighteenth century*, Great Dunham.

Tylor, Edward B., 1865, *Researches into the Early History of Mankind and the Development of Civilisation*, London.

Tylor, Edward B., 1871, *Primitive Culture: Researches into the Development of Mythology, Philosophy, Religion, Art and Custom*, 2 vols.

Wilson, Daniel, 1851, *The Archaeology and Prehistoric Annals of Scotland, Edinburgh.*

Wilson, Daniel, 1862, *Prehistoric Men*, 2 vols, Cambridge.

Wilson, Daniel, 1863, *Prehistoric Annals of Scotland.*

Index

Note this brief index covers main text only, not the appendices.
Italic figures indicate an illustration.
ff after a page number indicates 'and the following pages'.